SO-AIX-613

6 25 1

NO LONGER
PROPERTY OF
OLIN LIBRARY
WASHINGTON UNIVERSITY

NO LONGER
PROPERTY OF

METHUEN'S MONOGRAPHS
ON PHYSICAL SUBJECTS

General Editor: B. L. WORSNOP, PH.D

THE QUANTUM EQUATION AND
THE THEORY OF FIELDS

The Quantum Equation
and the Theory of Fields

H. T. FLINT

formerly Professor of Physics
Bedford College, London

LONDON : METHUEN & CO LTD
NEW YORK : JOHN WILEY & SONS INC

First published in 1966
© *1966 H. T. Flint*
Printed in Great Britain by
Spottiswoode, Ballantyne & Co Ltd
London and Colchester

Contents

Preface

The purpose of this work is to describe a theory of the physical world which includes the quantum theory and the theory of relativity as a complete whole. It is designed to show that the belief held by classical physicists that the same laws underlie the large- and small-scale phenomena can be maintained, although the belief must be expressed differently. The idea that the processes of Nature, which cannot be seen by the aided or unaided eye, can still be represented by models based on the experience resulting from direct observation must, at least for the present, be given up. Instead, reliance is placed on the mathematical form in which the laws of Nature are to be expressed. The principles governing the behaviour of models are replaced by the principle of covariance which is the basis of Einstein's theory of relativity. A knowledge of this theory is largely assumed for the purpose of this work.

The theory of relativity is a geometrical theory of the physical world. It can be said to rest upon the idea that the space of the physical world has certain properties expressible in terms of a particular form of geometry.

Space, time and matter are indissolubly related in this theory. The content of space (matter, energy, momentum, stress) determines the appropriate form of geometry and the relation between content and geometry, expressed quantitatively as a purely geometrical relation, is the law of gravitation.

The term space in this context means space–time, denoting the union in a four-dimensional geometry of three-dimensional space and time introduced by Minkowski in 1908.

It has been concluded that space–time has physical properties and it has been stated that if the physical properties of space could be removed geometrical properties would also disappear. There is, however, a difficulty concerning the physical properties of space, for such properties ought to be able to be measured. It is difficult to form any idea of how properties of space, in particular of empty space, could be measured, and when it is recalled that the aether of the classical theory has been replaced by space–time in the theory of relativity it would seem advisable to avoid reference to the properties of space for the same reason that reference to the properties of the aether is avoided. In physics the important concept is of spatial relations rather than of space, that is to say the concern is with location rather than with the properties of space. For this purpose certain parameters or coordinates are required as a starting point in the foundation of a physical theory and especially of a theory of mechanics. Relations between coordinates used in the process of location may be subject to certain limitations and they may take a geometrical form, but no property of what is described as space need be implied. The number of parameters required to found a successful theory can be described as the number of dimensions of space, but they need not necessarily be associated with a property of space. The importance lies in the use of parameters which can be explained physically and which can be made the subject of measurement.

Space has usually been described by means of continuous coordinates although the concept of a discontinuous geometry has been developed in which it is considered meaningless, from the point of view of the physical world, to introduce intervals of length and time below a certain minimum. In this case a cellular structure is attributed to space. If it is held consistently that the endowment of space with properties in this physical sense is to be avoided, the question of continuity or discontinuity must not be considered. It is the process of location which may have a continuous or discontinuous character and the coordinates used may have a continuous or discontinuous sequence of proper values.

Einstein's theory of relativity forms a background for all physical theory but it is essentially a theory of gravitation. Here the intimate relation between space–time and matter is actually the phenomenon of gravitation. Elsewhere, in spite of the change in outlook, new ideas and quantitative successes, its character is that of a formal theory in which success has resulted from the introduction of an appropriate formalism.

An outstanding success of this kind, comparable with the discovery of the law of gravitation, is Dirac's derivation of the fundamental equation of the quantum theory. He realized that Schroedinger's equation could not express correctly the fundamental quantum law because it did not satisfy the relativity principle of covariance. He was able, by an appeal to this principle, to introduce his well-known equation.

Maxwell's equations of the electromagnetic theory offer a striking example of the covariant character of relations expressing laws of Nature. It was by means of a study of transformations of space and time coordinates which leave the form of these equations unchanged that the Lorentz transformations were discovered. Einstein has written that with this discovery the theory of relativity had to follow. He was thinking particularly of the special theory of relativity but, with the discovery of the general theory, it became clear that the electromagnetic equations satisfied the wider relativistic principle of covariance. But the connection between the electromagnetic field and the geometry of space–time is not of the indissoluble character possessed by the gravitational field. The equations of electro-magnetism fit so easily into the gravitational scheme that they are like guests whose presence causes no disturbance.

In the belief that electromagnetic phenomena, like those of gravitation, should be regarded as the expression of some funda-mental property of the universe, Einstein and other writers have made suggestions which involve modifications of the original form of the theory of relativity. Of these the theory of H. Weyl and A. S. Eddington and the theory of T. Kaluza and O. Klein are of importance for the present work and they will be considered in some detail.

By means of them Dirac's equation and a generalization of it are derived from a theory of measurement, like that of Weyl but dif-ferently expressed. It is this which emphasizes the fact that the quantum theory is a theory of measurement and, taken with certain relations of H. Tetrode, reveals that phenomena on the small and large scales are the expression of fundamental characteristics of the physical world.

It is true that the general theory of relativity has hitherto played no part in the investigation and description of the world of small-scale phenomena and that the special theory has been sufficient. The value of an attempt to describe these phenomena within the general relativistic framework is to throw light upon the essential character of these phenomena and of the notation used to describe them.

The true character of the theory of relativity is not shown by the special theory, which, in spite of its wide application and of its contributions to knowledge, is largely a formalism. It is not until the coefficients (g_{mn}) of the line element of the geometrical system, used in the description, are considered as dependent upon the coordinates that it becomes possible to express the law of gravitation in the original simple form, $G_{mn}=0$. In the special theory the coefficients are constants and this equation is an identity. In the present work the same situation arises again. The theory of measurement leads to an equation of the form $K_{\mu}{}^{\mu}=0$ which is regarded as a law of nature. The equation is an identity in the case of constant matrices. It is the fundamental equation of the quantum theory leading to a general form of which Dirac's equation is a special case.

In attempting to describe the theory in terms of matrices with components dependent upon the coordinates it is not claimed that a satisfactory general relativistic matrix theory has been developed. The notation of the theory has been used in the case of variable matrices constructed in accordance with the notation described in the last chapter of the work. It is claimed that by this means the principle of relativity makes it possible to derive a general form of Dirac's equation, to give it a new significance and to reveal a new natural law.

The quantities introduced into the equation, for which there is scarcely any freedom of choice, are shown to be those which can be described as generators of the nuclear field in the theories hitherto proposed.

The consequence of the derivation of the quantum equation is the revelation of a unity pervading the world of small-scale phenomena and extending into that of phenomena on the large scale.

A disappointing feature is the occurrence of constants in the field equations, which might be expected to be world constants, for which the theory suggests no values.

The references given at the conclusion of each chapter are given partly to help the reader who may wish to consider the original works, but they are also given as an acknowledgement to the works of writers to whom the author is indebted.

H. T. FLINT

CHAPTER 1

The Theory of Relativity

It would appear that, since the time of the earliest recognition of the existence of an external world, space and time have been accepted as a background of knowledge. It has been held by some philosophers that without an *a priori* appreciation of these concepts knowledge is impossible. To the scientist, space and time have appeared as a framework with reference to which the positions and motion of bodies have been measured; it has been a stage upon which the phenomena of the physical world have presented themselves. These bodies and phenomena were regarded as having no effect upon the system of reference. The interest of the physicist lay in the location of points and extended bodies with respect to one another and in particular with reference to the framework.

The familiar system of Cartesian coordinates appeared to be the system of choice for the practical location of bodies in the physical world and it became evident that accurate quantitative results could be obtained by treating these coordinates as the parameters in the system of Euclidean geometry. This geometry was so closely associated with the description of physical phenomena and its applications had proved so valuable and accurate that it seemed a natural conclusion that these phenomena occurred in a space which could be described as Euclidean.

The system of localization can be compared with a graphical representation for which the nomenclature of geometry is available, but it should be kept in mind that the properties of what, in geometry, is described as space are not necessarily of the nature of those which can be measured in physics.

It is important that the parameters, or coordinates, used in the system of localization should have a physical meaning and should be measurable although they may be described in terms of conceptual geometry.

In Euclidean geometry, if a point P has coordinates (x, y, z) and a neighbouring point Q has coordinates $(x+dx, y+dy, z+dz)$, the interval or line element PQ is defined to be ds, where

$$ds^2 = dx^2 + dy^2 + dz^2. \tag{1.1}$$

This is recognized as the theorem of Pythagoras and ds is the length of the straight line PQ.

In addition to this concept of a metric characteristic of this geometry there is included the concept of parallelism. This is a definition of parallel lines and consists of the statement that, if a line PQ is displaced to P' Q' in such away that the coordinate differences of P and Q are unchanged, the lines PQ and $P'Q'$ (Fig. 1.1) are parallel.

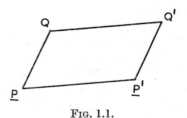

FIG. 1.1.

By the relation (1.1) they are also equal. This displacement from P to P' is described as a parallel displacement of the vector PQ between these two points. There is no limitation here to small vectors or small displacements but it is convenient on account of a generalization of the concepts of metric and of parallel displacement to use the differential notation.

If PQ be denoted by the vector $\mathbf{A}$ with components (A_x, A_y, A_z), and if the displacement PP' be denoted by the operator δ, the rule of parallel displacement of Euclidean geometry can be written as:

$$\delta A_x = 0, \quad \delta A_y = 0, \quad \delta A_z = 0.$$

If the line PQ has coordinate differences (dx, dy, dz), the parallel displacement of the line vector PQ is expressed by

$$\delta(dx) = 0, \quad \delta(dy) = 0, \quad \delta(dz) = 0.$$

It is convenient to express these relations briefly by

$$\delta(A_m) = 0 \quad (m = 1, 2, 3), \tag{1.2}$$

2

m taking the values 1, 2 or 3, corresponding to the coordinates (x, y, z) which may be represented conveniently by (x_m).

The line PP' may undergo a parallel displacement so that P comes to Q and the operator in this case may be denoted by d.

In the case of Euclidean geometry P' will at the same time arrive at Q' and the two displacements $\delta(PQ)$ and $d(PP')$ each mark out the closed figure $PP'QQ'$. This feature is characteristic of what is described as affine geometry.

The fact that in physics and in the experience of everyday life these two concepts of metric (1.1) and parallel displacement (1.2) have a general application has tended to conceal their purely geometrical character. The position with regard to them is that in arriving at a system of localization of points and bodies with respect to one another or to a frame of reference the notation of Euclidean geometry has been found useful over a wide domain. This has made the adoption of any other metric or concept of parallel displacement appear artificial. But from the purely mathematical point of view Euclidean geometry is one of a variety of systems, and, although it is more familiar and makes use of a simpler notation, it has no claim to being fundamentally less abstract than other geometries.

In the theory of special relativity Minkowski [1] showed that by including an additional parameter u as if it were a coordinate additional to (x, y, z) there was a great advantage in the use of the notation of a geometry of four dimensions in which the metric is defined by

$$ds^2 = dx^2 + dy^2 + dz^2 + du^2.$$

This may be written as

$$ds^2 = \sum (dx_n)^2 \quad (n = 1, 2, 3, 4) \tag{1.3}$$

and this extended form of Euclidean geometry is described as Galilean.

He showed that Einstein's conclusions concerning simultaneity, time dilation and the Fitzgerald contraction could be given a simple geometrical interpretation if the coordinate u were identified as $\sqrt{(-1)}\,ct$, where c denotes the velocity of light and t the time.

There is no justification for the assumption that a physical space exists which is four dimensional unless this is understood to mean simply that in the process of localization in space and time four

3

parameters are required or, at least, can form the basis of a useful notation.

It may be that the notation of Euclidean geometry is too restricted for application to the description of physical phenomena and indeed any known form of geometry may fail in this respect. But it may clearly be worthwhile to remove restrictions by the appeal to more general geometric forms.

In Einstein's theory of relativity the form of the line element, that is to say the metric, is generalized. Instead of the form (1.3)

$$ds^2 = \sum g_{mn} dx_m dx_n, \qquad (1.4)$$

where the summation is taken over the values $(1, 2, 3, 4)$ for m and n.

It is usual to write this equation without the sign of summation $\sum$ and to understand that, when a suffix such as m and n occurs twice in an expression like that on the right, summation is implied.

It is necessary to distinguish between two kinds of vector quantities in this case. These are contravariant and covariant quantities.

The components of a vector $\mathbf{A}$ of the former type are denoted typically by (A^m) and of the latter by (A_m). A line element is a contravariant vector so that its components are written in the form (dx^m). Equation (1.4) should thus be written in the form

$$ds^2 = g_{mn} dx^m dx^n \quad [2]. \qquad (1.5)$$

The coefficients (g_{mn}) are not constants but depend on the coordinates (x^m). In the case of Euclidean and Galilean geometry the coefficients are constant and have the values 0 or 1 $(g_{mn} = \delta_{mn})$, where δ_{mn} is the Kronecker delta quantity. In this case it is not necessary to distinguish between x^m and x_m or, in general, between the components of contravariant and covariant vectors. In Einstein's general theory of relativity the g_{mn} represent the existence of a gravitational field.

The definition of parallel displacement is also generalized in this case. Instead of the form (1.2) the change in a vector component as a result of a parallel displacement is assumed to depend linearly on the components (dx^m) of the displacement and on the components (A^m) of the vector. The expression which replaces (1.2) is

$$dA^n = -\Gamma_{lm}^n A^l dx^m \quad [3], \qquad (1.6)$$

and summation is implied over l and m, which can take the values $(1, 2, 3, 4)$. The coefficients (Γ_{lm}^n) are functions of the coordinates and play an important part in the description of physical phenomena, the values being given by

$$\Gamma^n_{lm} = \tfrac{1}{2}g^{nr}\left(\frac{\partial g_{mr}}{\partial x^l} + \frac{\partial x_{lr}}{\partial g^m} - \frac{\partial g_{lm}}{\partial x^r}\right) = g^{nr}\,\Gamma_{lm,\,r} \tag{1.7}$$

and the notation being that of Riemannian geometry.

It may be that further modifications will be necessary if physicists continue to think about and to describe natural phenomena in terms of geometry. Einstein's general theory of relativity is a theory of gravitation and, what may be described as the relativistic ideal of recognizing physical quantities as expressions of a geometrical background, has succeeded only in the case of gravitational phenomena. Thus, generalizations have appeared to remedy this defect but so far they have not been regarded as satisfactory. If the phenomena of the microscopic world are also to be included in a unified geometrical description, some radical changes in such relations as (1.5) and (1.6) are to be anticipated. It is the purpose of the present work to develop a theory leading to the introduction of such changes and showing the nature of their application and success.

Einstein's theory will not be developed here especially since the principles which underlie it will appear in the presentation of the theory of T. Kaluza and O. Klein, who modify it only in the addition of a parameter, which is treated as an additional coordinate. This theory is thus an application of Riemannian geometry of five dimensions to physics.

In spite of this addition of a new parameter, the principle of covariance of Einstein's theory will be maintained in the form in which it applies in the four-dimensional system which is, that the laws of physics must be expressed in a form independent of the space–time coordinates.

R. C. Tolman [4] in his work on Relativity, Thermodynamics and Cosmology writes on the subject of the justification and consequences of the adoption of this principle. His remarks may well be considered in relation to the case where an addition to the four coordinates of space–time is contemplated.

It is a firm conviction that physical behaviour is not affected by the system of reference used to describe it or that physical reality is independent of the coordinate system. This may be described as a physical principle of covariance.

2

5

In mathematics the language of the tensor calculus has been developed for the covariant expression of geometrical relations and, since it is desired to think of and to describe the laws of physics in terms of geometry, there seems to be no alternative to the adoption of this calculus for this description. As a consequence of this consideration it may be concluded that when the laws are expressed in this invariant form there is not of necessity any restriction on the nature of the laws.

In framing laws of physics, covariant equations must be used because in this way they are expressed independently of the coordinates.

So far this principle has led no one astray, on the contrary it has kept everyone on the right path. Thus, if new coordinates are added to the four-dimensional system, they must not affect it. The transformations to which they are subject may thus be expected to be restricted in order to preserve the correct form.

In the special theory of relativity the transformations of coordinates are linear, of the kind

$$x'_m = f_m(x_n). \tag{1.8}$$

This notation means that there are four equations, m having the values $(1,2,3,4)$ and four arbitrary functions (f_1, f_2, f_3, f_4). x_n is written as a typical coordinate, intended to indicate that the function depends on (x_1, x_2, x_3, x_4).

In the special theory each function is of the type

$$f_m(x_n) = a_1 x_1 + a_2 x_2 + a_3 x_3 + a_4 x_4,$$

where the a's are constants with different values for the different values of m.

This may be called a Lorentz transformation, although the well-known Lorentz equations are somewhat simpler. In the general case the functions f_m are of a general character.

If a vector quantity with components (A^m) is transformed by a change of coordinates (1.8) to become a vector with components (A'^m), the relation for the transformation is:

$$A'^m = \frac{\partial x'^m}{\partial x^a} A^n, \tag{1.9}$$

summation being over the values 1, 2, 3, 4 for n. This is for the contravariant vector and the corresponding relation for the covariant vector is:

$$A'_m = \frac{\partial x^n}{\partial x'^m} A_n. \tag{1.10}$$

The corresponding relations for tensors of the second rank of the contravariant, mixed and covariant types are:

$$\left.\begin{array}{l} T'^{mn} = \dfrac{\partial x'^m}{\partial x^k}\dfrac{\partial x'^n}{\partial x^l} T^{kl}, \quad T'^m_n = \dfrac{\partial x'^m}{\partial x^k}\dfrac{\partial x^l}{\partial x'^n} T^k_l \\[2ex] T'_{mn} = \dfrac{\partial x^k}{\partial x'^m}\dfrac{\partial x^l}{\partial x'^n} T_{kl}. \end{array}\right\} \tag{1.11}$$

Similar relations hold for tensors of higher rank. It was stated in the introduction that the truly relativistic character of Einstein's theory

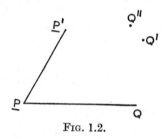

Fig. 1.2.

appears only in the theory of gravitation. In this case gravitational phenomena are manifestations of the geometrical properties of space–time. But electromagnetic phenomena have no similar indissoluble relationship with these properties. The question thus arises as to what kind of intimate relationship can be revealed in this case. The first suggestion on this point was made by H. Weyl in 1918, and to appreciate its significance the concept of parallel displacement in the form of equation (1.6) may be further examined.

Since we are concerned with the immediate neighbourhood of a point under consideration it is proposed to examine the change resulting in a vector as it undergoes a parallel displacement round an infinitesimal circuit near the point.

In the first place it is important to consider whether a parallel displacement of PQ along PP' and one of PP' along PQ bring Q and P' to the same point Q'. In Fig. 1.2 let the former bring Q to Q'. Let

7

the line element PQ have coordinates (dx^n) and PP' coordinates (δx^n).

The change in coordinates in the displacement is, according to (1.6),

$$\delta(dx^n) = -\Gamma^n_{lm} dx^l \delta x^m.$$

P has been displaced to P' so that the coordinate of Q' is

$$\delta x^n + dx^n - \Gamma^n_{lm} dx^l \delta x^m.$$

Similarly if PP' undergoes a parallel displacement along PQ, P' is brought to the point Q'' which has coordinates

$$dx^n + \delta x^n - \Gamma^n_{ml} \delta x^l dx^m.$$

Changing the suffixes

$$\Gamma^n_{lm} \delta x^l dx^m = \Gamma^n_{ml} \delta x^m dx,$$

so that if the points Q' and Q'' are the same,

$$\Gamma^n_{lm} = \Gamma^n_{ml}, \tag{1.12}$$

or the coefficients Γ are symmetric in l and m. This condition is assumed for the present purpose.

Suppose that a vector at a point P is subjected to a parallel displacement round a small loop back to the point P. Let the vector displaced have a typical component (A^m). The change dA^m for a small displacement with components (dx^n) is

$$dA^m = -\Gamma^m_{ln} A^l dx^n.$$

Integrating round the loop back to the starting point

$$\varDelta A^m = \oint dA^m = -\oint \Gamma^m_{ln} A^l dx^n.$$

By the application of Stokes' theorem this expression may be converted into a surface integral.

The familiar three-dimensional form of the theorem is

$$\int \mathbf{F}.d\mathbf{s} = \iint \operatorname{curl}\mathbf{F}.d\mathbf{S},$$

where the element of area $d\mathbf{S}$ has the x-component

$$dS = \delta y\, dz - \delta z\, dy,$$

which is the projection of the area $ABCD$, bounded by vectors AB and AD, with y and z components respectively δy and dz.

The form of this is readily generalized by writing

$$dS_x = dS_{23} = \delta x_2\, dx_3 - \delta x_3\, dx_2.$$

Thus

$$\operatorname{curl} \mathbf{F}.d\mathbf{S} = \left(\frac{\partial F_z}{\partial y} - \frac{\partial F_y}{\partial z}\right)(\delta y, dz - \delta z\, dy) + \ldots + \ldots$$

$$= \left(\frac{\partial F_3}{\partial x_2} - \frac{\partial F_2}{\partial x_3}\right) dS_{23} + \ldots$$

$$= \frac{1}{2}\left(\frac{\partial F_n}{\partial x_m} - \frac{\partial F_m}{\partial x_n}\right) dS_{mn},$$

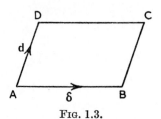

FIG. 1.3.

where summation is taken over $m, n = 1, 2, 3$ and the factor $\frac{1}{2}$ is required because in the cases such as $m = 2$, $n = 3$ and $m = 3$, $n = 2$ the same term occurs twice, thus extending the theorem to any member of dimensions:

$$\Delta A^m = -\frac{1}{2} \int \int \left\{ \frac{\partial}{\partial x^p}(\Gamma^m_{ln} A^l) - \frac{\partial}{\partial x^n}(\Gamma^m_{lp} A^l) \right\} dS^{pn}.$$

If the loop is small enough, this may be written in the form:

$$\Delta A^m = \frac{1}{2}\left(\frac{\partial}{\partial x^p}(\Gamma^m_{ln} A^l) - \frac{\partial}{\partial x^n}(\Gamma^m_{lp} A^l)\right) dS^{np}, \qquad (1.13)$$

and the values of the various quantities in this expression are appropriate to the neighbourhood of the point P.

Bearing in mind that the changes in the components (A^n) result from a parallel displacement, the expression in the bracket becomes:

$$\tfrac{1}{2}(\Gamma^m_{ln,\, p} - \Gamma^m_{lp,\, n} + \Gamma^m_{rp}\,\Gamma^r_{ln} - \Gamma^m_{rn}\,\Gamma^r_{lp})\, A^l,$$

where $\Gamma^m_{lp,\, n}$ denotes $\partial \Gamma^m_{lp}/\partial x^n$.

9

The factor of $\frac{1}{2}A^l$ is known as the Riemann–Christoffel tensor and is denoted by B^m_{lpn}.

$$\Delta A^m = \tfrac{1}{2}B^m_{lpn} A^l dS^{np}. \tag{1.14}$$

If the tensor (B^m_{lpn}) vanishes, there is no change in the components of the vector and, on returning to the starting point, the vector takes up its original position. This is a characteristic of Euclidean or flat space–time since the vanishing of this tensor is a necessary and sufficient condition for its existence.

In Riemannian geometry the line element is given by equation (1.5), the coefficients (g_{mn}) are not constant, as in the case of the geometry of flat space–time, and the Riemann–Christoffel tensor does not vanish. Thus on returning to the point P the components of the vector (A^m) have changed their values and the displaced vector no longer coincides with the original one. The question naturally arises whether the displaced vector itself has the same value as the original one. The length of the vector (A) is given by

$$A^2 = g_{mn} A^m A^n = A_n A^n$$

and, if $A_m \Delta A^m = 0$ there is no change of length.

$$A_n \Delta A^n = \tfrac{1}{2}A_n B^n_{lsr} A^l dS^{rs}$$
$$= \tfrac{1}{2}B_{lsrn} A^n A^l dS^{rs}, \tag{1.15}$$

where $B_{lsrn} = g_{nm} B^m_{lsr}$.

But since B_{lsrn} is antisymmetric in l and n, (1.15) vanishes owing to the presence of $A^n A^l$ which is symmetric in these affixes.

Thus the vector does not change its length although it returns with different components to the starting point and is, in consequence, inclined to the original direction. This feature of Riemannian geometry is associated with the adoption of the expression

$$A^2 = g_{mn} A^m A^n \tag{1.16}$$

for the square of the length of a vector.

This applies to all points and there is thus no change in the standard of measurement in passing by means of a parallel displacement from point to point.

It occurred to H. Weyl that a change of length might be contemplated in association with the idea of parallel displacement as well as a change of the components of a vector. He associated this change of length with the presence of an electromagnetic field and, just as the gravitational field expresses itself in terms of geometrical relations, so the electromagnetic field does so by means of a system of measurement or gauging.

This means that in the presence of an electromagnetic field the equation (1.15) cannot be considered to apply since the change of length vanishes with a parallel displacement defined in accordance with (1.6). Weyl's theory requires that $\oint A_m \Delta A^m \neq 0$ and consequently the change of length calculated for one path joining two points differs from that for another path joining the same two points. The change of length is thus dependent upon the path and is nonintegrable. It appears that in Weyl's theory either the definition of the length of a vector or of parallel displacement must be altered.

The form (1.16) for the length of a vector is retained but in order to compare vectors at different points a gauging factor might be introduced and a definition of equality of two vectors (A^m) at P and (A'^m) at P' might be suggested in the form

$$\lambda^2 g_{mn} A^m A^n = \lambda'^2 g'_{mn} A'^m A'^n \tag{1.17}$$

where λ and g_{mn} are the values of these functions at P and λ' and g'_{mn} their values of P'.

So long as comparisons of two vectors are made at the same point the gauging factor is of no consequence, since it cancels from the equation.

If the two vectors are situated at neighbouring points equation (1.17) becomes:

$$\delta(\lambda^2 A^2) = 0 \tag{1.18}$$

or

$$\frac{\delta\lambda^2}{\lambda^2} + \frac{\partial A^2}{A^2} = 0.$$

Thus if δA^2 depends upon the path of integration so also will λ^2 and the comparison of vectors at neighbouring points requires an arbitrary decision on the path to be taken in order to make the comparison. It is this arbitrariness which Weyl associates with the existence of an electromagnetic field. He writes for any vector

$$\frac{dA}{A} = \frac{1}{2}\frac{dA^2}{A^2} = -\phi_m dx^m \tag{1.19}$$

and identifies the vector (ϕ_m) with the vector and scalar potentials of the field. This identification is suggested by the fact that $\phi_m dx^m$ is non-integrable and Weyl's suggestion means that in a circuital parallel displacement of a vector in the presence of a gravitational and electromagnetic field not only the direction but also the magnitude of the vector is changed. In this way not only gravitation but also electromagnetism is incorporated into a system of geometry and measurement. It is clear that the definition of parallel displacement must be modified for in that already considered (1.6) there is no change of length.

In Eddington's presentation and extension of Weyl's suggestion this point is emphasized. He adopts the Riemannian expression (1.16) as the measure of the square of the length of a vector (A^m) at any point, regarding the adoption of a particular (g_{mn}) as equivalent to the adoption of a particular gauge-system.

A parallel displacement is defined as:

$$dA^n = -\Gamma'^n_{lm} A^l dx_m. \tag{1.20}$$

The Γ'^n_{lm} must differ from the Γ^n_{lm} already introduced since the latter are not associated with a change of length in a circuital displacement but only with a change of direction.

The change in A^2 resulting from the parallel displacement now becomes:

$$dA^2 = d(g_{mn} A^m A^n) = \frac{\partial g_{mn}}{\partial x^l} A^m A^n dx^l - g_{mn} \Gamma'^m_{pl} A^p A^n dx^l$$

$$- g_{mn} A^m \Gamma'^n_{pl} A^p dx^l$$

$$= \left(\frac{\partial g_{mn}}{\partial x^l} - g_{pn} \Gamma'^p_{ml} - g_{mp} \Gamma'^p_{nl} \right) A^m A^n dx^l.$$

If the quantity within the bracket is denoted by $2K_{mnl}$, writing $\Gamma'_{mln} = g_{pn} \Gamma'^p_{ml}$ and making use of equation (1.7)

$$2K_{mnl} = \frac{\partial g_{mn}}{\partial x^l} - \Gamma'_{mln} - \Gamma'_{nlm}$$

it follows that:

$$K_{mln} + K_{nlm} - K_{mnl} = \Gamma_{mnl} - \Gamma'_{mnl}. \tag{1.21}$$

Thus if the left-hand side of this equation be denoted by $-S_{mnl}$,

$$\Gamma'_{mnl} = \Gamma_{mnl} + S_{mnl}. \tag{1.22}$$

The expression for dA^2 can be written in the form

$$dA^2 = 2K_{mnl} A^m A^n dx^l. \tag{1.23}$$

This is a more general result than that of Weyl given in equation (1.19), which requires

$$K_{mnl} = -g_{mn}\phi_l. \tag{1.24}$$

Thus

$$S_{mnl} = g_{mn}\phi_l - g_{nl}\phi_m - g_{ml}\phi_n, \tag{1.25}$$

which, according to the relation (1.22), shows the dependence of the coefficients (Γ'_{mnl}) on the geometrical and gauging quantities (Γ_{mnl}) and (S_{mnl}) respectively. Einstein's interpretation of the coefficients (g_{mn}) and Weyl's interpretation of the coefficients (ϕ_n) as expressions of the phenomena of gravitation and electromagnetism, respectively, show how these phenomena are incorporated in the system of geometry and measurement.

These considerations lead to the important principle of gauge invariance. Since at any point comparison of lengths of vectors is unchanged by multiplication of all the coefficients (g_{mn}) by a function λ dependent on the coordinates, the description of events should be independent of the introduction of this factor. The square of the length A^2 can be replaced by the $\lambda^2 A^2$ and the length of a vector may be described equally well by $L^2 = \lambda^2 A^2$ as by A^2. But

$$\frac{dL^2}{L^2} = \frac{dA^2}{A^2} + \frac{d\lambda^2}{\lambda^2}.$$

Thus if

$$\frac{dA^2}{A^2} = -2\phi_i dx$$

it is possible to write

$$\frac{dL^2}{L^2} = -2\phi'_i dx^i = -2\phi_i dx^i + 2\frac{d(\log \lambda)}{dx^i} dx^i$$

and to replace ϕ_i by

$$\phi'_i = \phi_i - \frac{d}{dx_i}(\log \lambda). \tag{1.26}$$

Thus the principle must be introduced that the mathematical

expressions for laws of physics must be invariant with respect to the gauge transformation

$$g'_{mn} = \lambda^2 g_{mn}, \quad \phi'_i = \phi_i - \frac{d}{dx^i}(\log \lambda). \tag{1.27}$$

Maxwell's equations offer a well-known example of this. In this case the field intensities (B_{ik}) are derived from the electromagnetic potential (ϕ_i) by the relations

$$B_{ik} = \frac{\partial \phi_k}{\partial x^2} - \frac{\partial \phi_i}{\partial x^k}, \tag{1.28}$$

and it is evident that the addition of a gradient of a function to ϕ_i does not alter the value of B^{ik}. In fact

$$B_{ik} = \frac{\partial \phi'_k}{\partial x^i} - \frac{\partial \phi'_i}{\partial x^k}.$$

The second equation of (1.27) expresses the well-known arbitrary character of the electromagnetic vector potential.

The difficulty with Weyl's theory lies in its application to the physical world. According to it, it would be expected that a rigid rod and clock situated at a point P, which could be used to measure the space–time length, A, at P, would, after a parallel displacement to P', give a different measure at P' and that this new measure would depend on the displacement. This ambiguity would make it impossible to set up a standard at P and compare it with lengths at P'. Comparison of intervals of length and time at two such neighbouring places as P and P' would thus require a gauging device to be set up at all points of space. It is difficult to relate this to any observed phenomenon.

Einstein pointed out that in applying this principle to intervals of time it led to conclusions contrary to observation. Thus suppose a clock is at rest at a point P where conditions are static and suppose the clock records periods of time τ. In this case τ is the proper time and A has the value $c\tau$, where c is the velocity of light. In the static case ϕ_i vanishes for $i = 1, 2, 3$ and $\phi_4 = i\phi$, where ϕ is the electrostatic potential. Since $x^4 = ict$,

$$\frac{dl}{l} = \frac{d\tau}{\tau} = +c\,\phi\,dt$$

and

$$\tau = \tau_0 e^{+c\phi t}.$$

14

Now suppose that there are two similar clocks at P where the potential is ϕ and that for a time t one of them is taken to a place P', where the potential is ϕ', and is then brought back to P. The period τ' for this clock is then

$$\tau' = \tau e^{+c\phi' t}.$$

Thus $\tau'/\tau = \exp[i(\phi' - \phi)t]$ and it is implied that the period of a clock depends on the field which it has occupied.

Thus, in the case of atoms, orbital periodicities would depend on the electromagnetic fields the atoms had occupied in the course of their history. It would thus be impossible to associate with them those regularities which are evident from a study of the series of spectra.

These considerations led Weyl to express the view that 'the ideal process of parallel displacement of vectors has nothing to do with the actual behaviour of measuring rods and clocks. The metrical field cannot be defined directly by results taken with these instruments of measurement'.

According to the view expressed by Eddington the space–time of Weyl's theory is conceptual and physical phenomena are expressed in it in a way to be compared with a graphical representation. He suggests that the familiar representation of distances and directions in what is considered to be actual space is not essentially different from the representation of an isothermal or adiabatic on the space of a pressure-volume diagram.

The view taken in this book that the concern in physics is not the geometry of space but location in space comes close to these ideas.

Weyl's theory is not accepted here as one suitable for protraying a union between gravitation and electromagnetism.

It is suggested that Weyl's principle has been applied in the wrong place. Later on it will be shown that it can be used to unite the quantum theory with the theories of gravitation and electromagnetism and this seems an appropriate application of it, for both Weyl's theory and the quantum theory are essentially theories of measurement. The latter especially shows what can be measured and how it can be measured.

Bibliography

1. H. MINKOWSKI, 1920. *Raum u. Zeit. Das Relativitätsprinzip*, Lorentz-Einstein-Minkowski. Teubner.

2. A. S. EDDINGTON, 1930. *The Mathematical Theory of Relativity*, Chap. II, 2nd edn. Camb. Univ. Press.
3. H. WEYL, 1921. *Raum Zeit. Materie*, 4th edn. § 14.
   A. S. EDDINGTON, 1930. *The Mathematical Theory of Relativity*, Chap. VII, 2nd edn. Camb. Univ. Press.
   W. PAULI, JUN., 1921. *Relativitätstheorie*, § 65. B.G. Teubner.
4. R. C. TOLMAN, 1934. *The General Theory of Relativity*, Chap. VI, 1st edn. §§ 72, 73. Oxford, Clarendon Press.

CHAPTER 2

The Theory of Kaluza and Klein

In 1921 T. Kaluza [1] proposed a theory for the unification of gravitation and electromagnetism differing from that of H. Weyl.

He based his work on the ideas of Einstein and found that these could be followed closely if a five-dimensional coordinate system were adopted instead of the four-dimensional system of the general theory of relativity.

The appropriate line element, $d\sigma$, in this case is given by the relation:

$$d\sigma^2 = \gamma_{\mu\nu} dx^\mu dx^\nu \quad (\mu, \nu = 1, 2, 3, 4, 5). \tag{2.1}$$

Greek letters will now be used as suffixes for five-dimensional quantities and Latin letters for the four-dimensional ones.

The transformations of the five coordinates have not the generality corresponding to those of the four-dimensional system of Einstein's theory. The limitations imposed on the transformations permitted to the fifth coordinate are such as to make it possible to retain the four-dimensional principle of covariance and to satisfy the requirements of a physical theory. The difficulty facing this theory is the association of a physical concept with a fifth dimension. The same difficulty occurs in the four-dimensional theory of relativity, but at least the coordinate x^4 can be given the significance of time. There can be no objection to the introduction of parameters into the theories of the physical world provided that they can be interpreted physically and, especially, provided that they can be subjected to measurement. Distaste and difficulty arise if analogies are made which lead to confusion through being taken too literally. The use of Kaluza's five-dimensional system is accepted in accordance with the views expressed in the introduction as a system of location.

Coordinate transformations

In the general theory of relativity the four coordinates (x^m) may be subjected to the transformations

$$x'^m = f_m(x^n), \qquad (2.2)$$

where the four functions, of which f_m is typical, are arbitrary and dependent on the four coordinates, x^n being a brief representation of them.

The corresponding transformations in a five-dimensional system are

$$x'^\mu = f_\mu(x^\nu), \qquad (2.3)$$

where there are now five functions dependent upon five coordinates.

This degree of arbitrariness is not required for the present purpose and, if adopted, it would introduce into the theory many quantities difficult to determine. The purpose is served if the transformation for the fifth coordinate is restricted by the adoption of the relation

$$x'^5 = x^5 + f_5(x^n), \qquad (2.4)$$

where f_5 is an arbitrary function dependent upon the four coordinates (x^n), $n = 1, 2, 3, 4$. This kind of transformation may be compared with that adopted for an additional coordinate in the projective theory of relativity of O. Veblen.

The use of these transformations has some simple consequences. Thus, if (A^μ) denotes a five-vector, the components (A^m) with $m \neq 5$ transform as follows:

$$A'^m = \frac{\partial x'^m}{\partial x^\mu} A^\mu = \frac{\partial x'^m}{\partial x^n} A^n, \qquad (2.5)$$

with x'^m independent of x^5 in the transformation. The four components (A^m) of the five-vector thus form a contravariant four-vector.

Another simple case is that of the fifth covariant component for which

$$A'_5 = \frac{\partial x^\mu}{\partial x'^5} A_\mu$$

and since x^m does not contain x'^5 in the transformation

$$A'_5 = \frac{\partial x^5}{\partial x'^5} A_5 = A_5, \qquad (2.6)$$

from which it follows that A'_5 transforms like a scalar quantity in four dimensions.

Tensors and vectors of higher rank may be treated in the same way. In the case of a contravariant tensor of the second rank

$$A'^{\mu\nu} = \frac{\partial x'^{\mu}}{\partial x^{\rho}} \frac{\partial x'^{\nu}}{\partial x^{\sigma}} A^{\rho\sigma} \tag{2.7}$$

gives for the case where $\mu, \nu = m, n$

$$A'^{mn} = \frac{\partial x'^{m}}{\partial x^{r}} \frac{\partial x'^{n}}{\partial x^{s}} A^{rs} \tag{2.8}$$

so that the components (A^{mn}) form a four-dimensional tensor.

The case of the components $(A^{m}{}_{5})$ of the corresponding mixed tensor $(A^{\mu}{}_{\nu})$ is interesting. For these components

$$A'^{m}{}_{5} = \frac{\partial x'^{m}}{\partial x^{\mu}} \frac{\partial x^{\nu}}{\partial x'^{5}} A^{\mu}{}_{\nu} \tag{2.9}$$

$$= \frac{\partial x'^{m}}{\partial x^{l}} A^{l}{}_{5}$$

since $\partial x'^{m}/\partial x^{5}$ and $\partial x^{n}/\partial x'^{5}$ vanish.

Thus $(A^{m}{}_{5})$ forms a four-dimensional vector. Similarly it may be shown that A_{55} is a scalar in a four-dimensional system.

It is sometimes convenient to use small letters to denote the components of the four-dimensional quantities related to the five-dimensional ones. Thus, in the case of a vector, the four-dimensional vector (a^{m}) is related to the five-dimensional (A^{μ}) where

$$a^{m} = A^{m}. \tag{2.10}$$

Similarly a four-dimensional tensor (a^{mn}) is related to $(A^{\mu\nu})$ where

$$a^{mn} = A^{mn}. \tag{2.11}$$

The coefficients $(\gamma_{\mu\nu})$ of the line element (2.1) form a five-dimensional covariant tensor and with them is associated a contravariant tensor $(\gamma^{\mu\nu})$. These tensors have the same properties as the corresponding four-dimensional tensors (g_{mn}) and (g^{mn}).

A contravariant five-vector (A^{μ}) is related to a covariant companion vector by the relations:

$$A_{\mu} = \gamma_{\mu\nu} A^{\nu}, \quad A^{\mu} = \gamma^{\mu\nu} A_{\nu},$$

the summation occurring over the numbers (1–5) and tensors are similarly related exactly as in four dimensions.

In accordance with the relation (2.11) the components (γ^{mn}) form a four-dimensional tensor and this will be identified with the tensor (g^{mn}). Thus

$$\gamma^{mn} = g^{mn}, \tag{2.12}$$

moreover from what has been stated above concerning the component A_{55}, it follows that the component γ_{55} is a four-dimensional scalar quantity.

A result of some importance is that the expression

$$\left(A_m - \frac{\gamma_{m5}}{\gamma_{55}} A_5\right)$$

transforms like a four-dimensional vector, where A_m and A_5 are the components of any vector.

To prove this it is noted that the transformed quantity

$$A'_m - \frac{\gamma'_{m5}}{\gamma'_{55}} A'_5 = A'_m - \frac{\gamma'_{m5}}{\gamma_{55}} A_5.$$

since γ_{55} and A_5 are scalars. But

$$A'_m - \frac{\gamma'_{m5}}{\gamma_{55}} A_5 = \frac{\partial x^\mu}{\partial x'^m} A_\mu - \frac{\partial x^\mu}{\partial x'^m} \frac{\partial x^\nu}{\partial x'^5} \gamma_{\mu\nu} \frac{A_5}{\gamma_{55}}$$

$$\frac{\partial x^\mu}{\partial x'^m} A_\mu = \frac{\partial x^n}{\partial x'^m} A_n + \frac{\partial x^5}{\partial x'^m} A_5$$

$$\frac{\partial x^\mu}{\partial x'^m} \frac{\partial x^\nu}{\partial x'^5} \gamma_{\mu\nu} \frac{A_5}{\gamma_{55}} = \frac{\partial x^\mu}{\partial x'^m} \frac{\partial x^5}{\partial x'^5} \gamma_{\mu 5} \frac{A_5}{\gamma_{55}}$$

since

$$\frac{\partial x^n}{\partial x'^5} = 0.$$

Since also $\partial x^5 / \partial x'^5 = 1$, the quantity on the left-hand side becomes

$$\frac{\partial x^n}{\partial x'^m} \gamma_{n5} \frac{A_5}{\gamma_{55}} + \frac{\partial x^5}{\partial x'^m} A_5.$$

Thus

$$A'_m - \frac{\gamma'_{m5}}{\gamma'_{55}} A'_5 = \frac{\partial x^n}{\partial x'^m} \left(A_n - \frac{\gamma_{n5}}{\gamma_{55}} A_5\right) \tag{2.13}$$

from which it appears that $[A_m - (\gamma_{m5}/\gamma_{55})A_5]$ transforms like a four-dimensional vector.

This quantity will be assumed to be the four-dimensional covariant vector corresponding to the five-vector (A_μ) and it will be denoted by

$$a_m = A_m - \frac{\gamma_{m5}}{\gamma_{55}} A_5. \qquad (2.14)$$

The contravariant four-vector (a^m) defined in the relation (2.10) and the vector (a_m) are assumed to be companion vectors, i.e.

$$a_m = g_{mn} a^n.$$

From these assumptions a relation between the coefficients $(\gamma_{\mu\nu})$ and (g_{mn}) can be obtained.

For

$$A_m - \frac{\gamma_{m5}}{\gamma_{55}} A_5 = a_m = g_{mn} a^n$$

$$\gamma_{m\lambda} A^\lambda - \frac{\gamma_{m5}}{\gamma_{55}} A_5 = g_{mn} a^n$$

$$(\gamma_{mn} - g_{mn}) A^n = \frac{\gamma_{m5}}{\gamma_{55}} (A_5 - \gamma_{55} A^5).$$

But

$$A_5 = \gamma_{5\mu} A^\mu = \gamma_{55} A^5 + \gamma_{5n} A^n$$

so that

$$(\gamma_{mn} - g_{mn}) A^n = \frac{\gamma_{m5} \gamma_{n5}}{\gamma_{55}} A^n;$$

since the coefficients are symmetric in the indices $\gamma_{5n} = \gamma_{n5}$. This relation must be true for all vectors and consequently

$$g_{mn} = \gamma_{mn} - \frac{\gamma_{m5} \gamma_{n5}}{\gamma_{55}}. \qquad (2.15)$$

From the relations (2.10) and (2.14) it is possible to associate four- and five-dimensional components of tensors.

A tensor component of the second rank is subject to the same law of transformation as the product of two-vector components. Thus the component $A^{\mu\nu}$ is transformed in the same way as $A^\mu B^\nu$, where A^μ

and B^ν are components of two five-vectors. A similar remark applies to mixed and covariant tensors. Thus $A^\mu{}_\nu$ has the same law of transformation as $A^\mu B_\nu$ and $A_{\mu\nu}$ the same as $A_\mu B_\nu$.

The relation (2.11) can in this way be derived from the assumption that (A^m) forms a four-dimensional contravariant vector. This means that $A^m B^n$, where B^n is a component of a similar vector, transforms like $a^m b^n$, where a^m and b^n are components of four-vectors.

Thus the components (A^{mn}) of a five-dimensional contravariant tensor transform like the components (a^{mn}) of a four-dimensional one and the two tensors can be described as associated tensors.

Similarly, since A_5 is a scalar quantity from the point of view of four dimensions, the tensor components $(A^m{}_5)$ form a four-vector.

The form of the association of covariant tensor components can be obtained from the relation (2.14).

From a consideration of the product

$$a_m b_n = \left(A_m - \frac{\gamma_{m5}}{\gamma_{55}} A_5\right)\left(B_n - \frac{\gamma_{n5}}{\gamma_{55}} B_5\right),$$

and by replacing products by tensor components, it appears that

$$a_{mn} = A_{mn} - \frac{\gamma_{m5}}{\gamma_{55}} A_{5n} - \frac{\gamma_{n5}}{\gamma_{55}} A_{m5} + \frac{\gamma_{m5}\gamma_{n5}}{\gamma_{55}^2} A_{55}. \qquad (2.16)$$

The quantity on the right-hand side transforms like a covariant tensor and (a_{mn}) is the covariant tensor associated with the contravariant (a_{mn}), that is to say

$$a_{mn} = g_{mk} g_{nl} a^{kl}.$$

A reason will be given later on for regarding $A_5/\sqrt{(\gamma_{55})}$ as the four-dimensional counterpart of the component A_5 of the covariant five-vector. This will be denoted by $a_.$.

To every five-vector (A^μ) a four-dimensional vector (a^m) is associated together with a scalar $a_.$, where

$$a^m = A^m, \quad a_. = A_5/\sqrt{(\gamma_{55})}. \qquad (2.17)$$

From these relations those existing between associated quantities in four and five dimensions can be derived. For example

$$A^m B_5 = a^m \sqrt{(\gamma_{55})} b_.,$$

22

so that a mixed tensor component $A^m{}_5$ is associated with a four-dimensional vector $a^m{}_.$ by the relation

$$a^m{}_. = A^m{}_5/\sqrt{(\gamma_{55})}. \tag{2.18}$$

The component A_{55} of a five-dimensional covariant tensor is in the same way associated with a four-dimensional scalar

$$a_{..} = A_{55}/\gamma_{55}. \tag{2.19}$$

From the expression (2.14) it follows that the relation between covariant components with suffix 5 and their four-dimensional counterparts is

$$A_{m5} = \sqrt{(\gamma_{55})}\,(a_{m.} + \gamma_{m5}a_{..}), \quad a_{m.} = \frac{1}{\sqrt{(\gamma_{55})}}\left(A_{m5} - \frac{\gamma_{m5}}{\gamma_{55}}A_{55}\right). \tag{2.20}$$

The components A^5, A^{5m} and A^{m5} are readily expressed in terms of four-dimensional quantities. Thus

$$A_5 = \gamma_{5\mu}A^\mu = \gamma_{55}A^5 + \gamma_{5m}A^m$$

$$A^5 = \frac{A_5 - \gamma_{5m}A^m}{\gamma_{55}}$$

$$= \frac{a_.}{\sqrt{(\gamma_{55})}} - \frac{\gamma_{5m}}{\gamma_{55}}a^m \tag{2.21}$$

In the same way

$$A^{5m} = \frac{A_5{}^m - \gamma_{5n}A^{mn}}{\gamma_{55}} = \frac{a_.{}^m}{\sqrt{(\gamma_{55})}} - \frac{\gamma_{5m}}{\gamma_{55}}a^{nm} \tag{2.22}$$

and

$$A^{m5} = \frac{A^m{}_5 - \gamma_{5n}A^{mn}}{\gamma_{55}} = \frac{a^m{}_.}{\sqrt{(\gamma_{55})}} - \frac{\gamma_{5n}}{\gamma_{55}}a^{mn} \tag{2.23}$$

Also

$$A_{55} = \gamma_{5\mu}A_5{}^\mu = \gamma_{55}A_5{}^5 + \gamma_{5m}A_5{}^m$$

and thus

$$A_5{}^5 = \frac{A_{55}}{\gamma_{55}} - \frac{\gamma_{5m}}{\gamma_{55}}A_5{}^m = a_{..} - \frac{\gamma_{5m}}{\sqrt{(\gamma_{55})}}a_.{}^m \tag{2.24}$$

Finally, from $\gamma_{5\mu} A^{5\mu} = A^5{}_5$ after substitution of $A_5{}^5$ and A^{m5}, by means of equations (2.14) and (2.13) it follows that

$$A^{55} = \frac{1}{\gamma_{55}{}^2} (A_{55} - \gamma_{5m} A_5{}^m - \gamma_{m5} A^m{}_5 + \gamma_{m5}\gamma_{5n} A^{mn}) \qquad (2.25)$$

$$= \frac{1}{\gamma_{55}} a_{..} - \frac{1}{\sqrt{(\gamma_{55})}} \frac{\gamma_{5m}}{\gamma_{55}} (a_.{}^m + a^m{}_.) + \frac{\gamma_{m5}\gamma_{5n}}{\gamma_{55}{}^2} a^{mn},$$

since the coefficients $(\gamma_{\mu\nu})$ are symmetric in μ and ν.

The geodesic and values of the coefficients $(\gamma_{\mu\nu})$

If two points, P_1 and P_2, of a continuum be joined by a line of which an element of length is denoted by ds, its length is denoted by

$$l = \int_{P_1}^{P_2} ds. \qquad (2.26)$$

The line for which this length has a stationary value is described as a geodesic, the condition satisfied being written in the form

$$\delta \int_{P_1}^{P_2} ds = 0. \qquad (2.27)$$

In the case in which the geometry is Euclidean the geodesic is the straight line joining P_1 and P_2 and the length of the line joining these points has a minimum value.

Differential equations for the geodesic are obtained from the condition (2.27) by the method applied to stationary integrals. If a function L depends on the variables (x, y, z) and their first differential coefficients with respect to a parameter λ, upon which they depend, i.e.

$$L = L\left(x, y, z, \frac{dx}{d\lambda}, \frac{dy}{d\lambda}, \frac{dz}{d\lambda}\right),$$

the condition

$$\delta \int_{\lambda_1}^{\lambda_2} L \, d\lambda = 0,$$

leads to the equation

$$\frac{d}{d\lambda}\frac{\partial L}{\partial \dot{x}} - \frac{\partial L}{\partial x} = 0 \qquad (2.28)$$

and to two similar equations in y and z, where $\dot{x}$ denotes $dx/d\lambda$ and similarly, $\dot{y}$ and $\dot{z}$ denote $dy/d\lambda$ and $dz/d\lambda$ respectively.

If λ is taken to be the time t the variation takes the form

$$\delta \int_{t_1}^{t_2} \frac{ds}{dt}.dt = 0$$

and in Euclidean space

$$L = \frac{ds}{dt} = (\dot{x}^2+\dot{y}^2+\dot{z}^2)^{1/2} = v$$

hence L does not contain the coordinates explicitly the differential equations of the geodesic are

$$\frac{d}{dt}\left(\frac{\partial L}{\partial \dot{x}}\right) = \frac{d}{dt}\left(\frac{\dot{x}}{v}\right) = 0 \qquad (2.29)$$

and the equations in y and z.

When there are no forces acting upon the body v is constant and the equations of the geodesic are

$$\frac{d^2 x}{dt^2} = \frac{d^2 y}{dt^2} = \frac{d^2 z}{dt^2} = 0. \qquad (2.30)$$

The equations express Newton's first law of motion that a particle subject to no forces moves in a straight line.

This is a particular case of a more general statement that a particle subject to no forces moves along a geodesic. In the theory of relativity gravitational force is regarded as an expression of the geometry of space and a particle in a gravitational field is not strictly subjected to forces. It is, in the wider sense in which Riemannian geometry replaces Euclidean geometry, a free particle and it is assumed that its equation of motion is a geodesic given by the condition (2.29) with

$$ds^2 = g_{mn} dx^m dx^n.$$

If now L has the value:

$$L = \left(g_{mn} \frac{dx^m}{d\lambda}\frac{dx^n}{d\lambda}\right)^{1/2},$$

the condition is

$$\delta \int_{\lambda_1}^{\lambda_2} L d\lambda = 0,$$

where the coordinates depend on the parameter λ.

The equation to the curve will be taken to be $x = f_1(\tau)$, etc., where the parameter τ is the proper time, i.e. $ds^2 = -c^2 d\tau^2$. Thus the equations of the geodesic are:

$$\frac{d}{d\tau}\frac{\partial L}{\partial \dot{x}^r} = \frac{\partial L}{\partial x^r}$$

where $\dot{x}^m = dx^m/d\tau$, and L is written in the form:

$$L = (g_{mn}\dot{x}^m \dot{x}^n)^{1/2} = ic$$

$$\frac{\partial L}{\partial \dot{x}^r} = \frac{g_{rn}\dot{x}^n}{L^{1/2}} = \frac{1}{ic}g_{rn}\dot{x}^n$$

$$\frac{\partial L}{\partial x^r} = \frac{1}{2L^{1/2}}\frac{\partial g_{mn}}{\partial x^r}\dot{x}^m \dot{x}^n.$$

Thus
$$\frac{d}{d\tau}(g_{rn}\dot{x}^n) = \frac{1}{2}\frac{\partial g_{mn}}{\partial x^r}\dot{x}^m \dot{x}^n. \tag{2.31}$$

In the theory of five dimensions a similar equation will hold and τ, the proper time, will again be taken as the parameter.

Thus with $\dot{x}^\mu = dx^\mu/d\tau$, the equation of the geodesic is

$$\frac{d}{d\tau}(\gamma_{\rho\nu}\dot{x}^\nu) = \frac{1}{2}\frac{\partial \gamma_{\mu\nu}}{\partial x^\rho}\dot{x}^\mu \dot{x}^\nu. \tag{2.32}$$

Another way of deriving the equation of the geodesic is to apply a parallel displacement to the vector tangent to a curve at a point P. The components of this vector are $(dx^\mu/d\tau)$ and the geodesic is the curve for which the change in these components in passing from P to a neighbouring point P' is given by a parallel displacement.

In the five-dimensional continuum the five dimensional components of the Christoffel bracket expressions will be denoted by $(\Delta^\mu_{\rho\sigma})$ (cf. 1.7)

$$\Delta^\mu_{\rho\sigma} = \gamma^{\mu\lambda}\Delta_{\rho\sigma\lambda} = \frac{1}{2}\gamma^{\mu\lambda}\left(\frac{\partial \gamma_{\lambda\rho}}{\partial x^\sigma} + \frac{\partial \gamma_{\lambda\sigma}}{\partial x_\rho} - \frac{\partial \gamma_{\rho\sigma}}{\partial x^\lambda}\right). \tag{2.33}$$

The equation of the geodesic is therefore:

$$d\left(\frac{dx^\mu}{d\tau}\right) = -\Delta^\mu_{\rho\sigma}\frac{dx^\rho}{d\tau}dx^\sigma$$

or
$$\frac{d^2 x^\mu}{d\tau^2} = -\Delta^\mu_{\rho\sigma}\dot{x}^\rho \dot{x}^\sigma, \tag{2.34}$$

which is another form of equation (2.32).

In the theory of relativity the geodesic is identified with the path of a particle in a gravitational field. In Kaluza's theory the geodesic is identified with the path of a charged particle in a gravitational and electromagnetic field.

In the classical theory, neglecting gravitation, the equation of motion of a particle of mass M carrying a charge of q electrostatic units is

$$M\frac{d^2\mathbf{r}}{dt^2} = q\left(\mathbf{E}+\frac{\mathbf{v}\times\mathbf{B}}{c}\right), \tag{2.35}$$

where $\mathbf{E}$ denotes the electric intensity and $\mathbf{B}$ the magnetic induction, $\mathbf{v}$ is the velocity of the charged particle.

$\mathbf{E}$ and $\mathbf{B}$ can be derived from the scalar potential, ϕ, and the vector potential $\mathbf{A}$ by means of the formulae

$$\mathbf{E} = -\operatorname{grad}\phi-\frac{1}{c}\frac{d\mathbf{A}}{dt}, \quad \mathbf{B} = \operatorname{curl}\mathbf{A}. \tag{2.36}$$

It is convenient to introduce the notation of the theory of relativity by writing:

$$A_x = \phi_1, \quad A_y = \phi_2, \quad A_z = \phi_3, \quad \phi = -i\phi_4. \tag{2.37}$$

The equations (2.36) can then be represented by

$$B_{mn} = \frac{\partial\phi_n}{\partial x^m}-\frac{\partial\phi_m}{\partial x^n}, \tag{2.38}$$

m and n having the values 1, 2, 3, 4, by writing

$$\left.\begin{array}{lll}B_{23} = B_x, & B_{31} = B_y, & B_{12} = B_z, \\ B_{41} = iE_x, & B_{42} = iE_y, & B_{43} = iE_z,\end{array}\right\} \tag{2.39}$$

remembering that $x^4 = ict$.

The quantities (ϕ_m) form a covariant four-vector and the (B_{mn}) a covariant tensor of the second rank. The x-component of equation (2.35) is:

$$M\frac{d^2x}{dt^2} = q\left(E_x+\frac{v_yB_z-v_zB_y}{c}\right), \tag{2.40}$$

and, writing

$$v_1 = \frac{dx}{dt}, \quad v_2 = \frac{dy}{dt}, \quad v_3 = \frac{dz}{dt}, \quad v_4 = \frac{dx^4}{dt} = ic, \tag{2.41}$$

or generally $v_m = dx_m/dt$, the right-hand side of this expression becomes

$$\frac{q}{c}\left(B_{12}\frac{dx^2}{dt} + B_{13}\frac{dx^3}{dt} + B_{14}\frac{dx^4}{dt} \right),$$

remembering that $B_{mn} = -B_{nm}$.

Thus a component of the equation of motion may be written in the form:

$$M\frac{d^2 x^m}{dt^2} = \frac{q}{c}B_{mn}\frac{dx^n}{dt}.$$

If M_0 denotes the rest mass of the particle and $d\tau$ an element of proper time, $M = M_0(dt/d\tau)$, and the equation becomes

$$\frac{d}{d\tau}\left(M_0\frac{dx^m}{d\tau} \right) = \frac{q}{c}B_{mn}\frac{dx^n}{d\tau}. \tag{2.42}$$

This is the form of the equation appropriate in the theory of special relativity. In the presence of a gravitational field the form appropriate to the general theory must be adopted.

Thus the equation of motion to be identified with the geodesic in five dimensions is:

$$M_0\left\{ \frac{d}{d\tau}\left(g_{mn}\frac{dx^n}{d\tau} \right) - \frac{1}{2}\frac{\partial g_{rs}}{\partial x^m}\frac{dx^r}{d\tau}\frac{dx^s}{d\tau} \right\} = \frac{q}{c}B_{mn}\frac{dx^n}{d\tau}. \tag{2.43}$$

In equation (2.32) the substitution $\rho = m$ should give an equation identical with (2.43). The case $\rho = 5$ gives a new result not contained in (2.43).

It is assumed that the coefficients $(\gamma_{\mu\nu})$ are independent of the fifth coordinate and that γ_{55} is a constant independent of all the coordinates.

In the case of $\rho = 5$ the right-hand side of (2.32) vanishes and thus

$$\gamma_{5\nu}\dot{x}^\nu = a \quad (a \text{ constant}). \tag{2.44}$$

When $\rho = m$ the left-hand side of (2.32) becomes

$$\frac{d}{d\tau}(\gamma_{mn}\dot{x}^n + \gamma_{m5}\dot{x}^5)$$

and thus, substituting for γ_{mn} from the relation (2.15),

$$\frac{d}{d\tau}(g_{mn}\dot{x}^n) + \frac{d}{d\tau}\left(\frac{\gamma_{m5}\gamma_{n5}}{\gamma_{55}}\dot{x}^n + \gamma_{m5}\dot{x}^5\right)$$

or

$$\frac{d}{d\tau}(g_{mn}\dot{x}^n) + \frac{d}{d\tau}\left(\frac{\gamma_{m5}}{\gamma_{55}}\right)a.$$

The right-hand side can be written in the form:

$$\frac{1}{2}\frac{\partial}{\partial x^m}\left(g_{rs} + \frac{\gamma_{r5}\gamma_{s5}}{\gamma_{55}}\right)\dot{x}^r\dot{x}^s + \frac{\partial\gamma_{5r}}{\partial x^m}\dot{x}^5\dot{x}^r + \frac{1}{2}\frac{\partial\gamma_{55}}{\partial x^m}(\dot{x}^5)^2$$

which reduces to

$$\frac{1}{2}\frac{\partial g_{rs}}{\partial x^m}\dot{x}^r\dot{x}^s + \frac{1}{\gamma_{55}}\frac{\partial\gamma_{r5}}{\partial x^m}\dot{x}^r a$$

since $a = \gamma_{5\nu}\dot{x}^\nu = \gamma_{5r}\dot{x}^r + \gamma_{55}\dot{x}^5$ and $\partial\gamma_{55}/\partial x^m$ vanishes.

The equation of the geodesic thus becomes:

$$\frac{d}{d\tau}\left(g_{mn}\frac{dx^n}{d\tau}\right) - \frac{1}{2}\frac{\partial g_{rs}}{\partial x^m}\dot{x}^r\dot{x}^s = \frac{a}{\gamma_{55}}\dot{x}^n\left(\frac{\partial\gamma_{n5}}{\partial x^m} - \frac{\partial\gamma_{m5}}{\partial x^n}\right), \qquad (2.45)$$

the adjustment of dummy suffixes being made for the sake of comparison with equation (2.43).

From the fact that

$$B_{mn} = \frac{\partial\phi_n}{\partial x^m} - \frac{\partial\phi_m}{\partial x^n}$$

for the equations to become identical γ_{m5}/γ_{55} and γ_{n5}/γ_{55} must be proportional to ϕ_m and ϕ_n respectively.

Let γ_{m5}/γ_{55} be placed equal to $\alpha\phi_m$ and similarly γ_{n5}/γ_{55} equal to $\alpha\phi_n$, α will be assumed to be a universal constant. Thus comparing the equations (2.43) and (2.45) it is evident that

$$a\alpha = q/M_0 c.$$

There have been different ways of making this identification, but an idea suggested by the wave-particle theory of matter will serve as a guide here.

The expression, $d\sigma^2 = \gamma_{\mu\nu}dx^\mu dx^\nu$, can be written in the form:

$$d\sigma^2 = \left(\gamma_{mn} - \frac{\gamma_{m5}\gamma_{n5}}{\gamma_{55}}\right)dx^m dx^n + \frac{(\gamma_{5\mu}dx^\mu)^2}{\gamma_{55}}$$

$$= g_{mn}dx^m dx^n + \frac{(\gamma_{5\mu}dx^\mu)^2}{\gamma_{55}}. \qquad (2.46)$$

From the definition (1.5) of the four-dimensional line element and from equation (2.44), it follows that

$$d\sigma^2 = ds^2 + \frac{a^2}{\gamma_{55}} d\tau^2. \tag{2.47}$$

In the theory of relativity all particles in a gravitational field travel along geodesics and a ray of light follows the path of a null-geodesic. Another way of stating this is that all photons travel along null-geodesics, which means that along the path of the photon

$$ds^2 = 0 \tag{2.48}$$

is a special characteristic of the geodesic which is the path of a photon. All photons, whatever their frequency or energy, travel along null-geodesics.

In quantum mechanics particles of matter behave like waves and it seems a natural suggestion that in the present theory the dual character of matter should find its expression in the assumption that all particles, whatever their mass or charge, should travel along null-geodesics. The special characteristic now being

$$d\sigma^2 = 0 \quad [3]. \tag{2.49}$$

It will be noticed that if dx_5 be written for the fifth component of the covariant vector associated with the line element (dx^μ), then

$$dx_5 = \gamma_{\mu 5} dx^\mu, \tag{2.50}$$

and thus from (2.46)

$$d\sigma^2 = ds^2 + \frac{dx_5^2}{\gamma_{55}}. \tag{2.51}$$

Thus on a null-geodesic

$$dx_5^2 = -\gamma_{55} ds^2$$

and since

$$ds^2 = -c^2 d\tau^2,$$

it follows that on this geodesic,

$$dx_5 = \sqrt{(\gamma_{55})}\, c\, d\tau. \tag{2.52}$$

This relation associates the fifth coordinate with the proper time and gives a physical meaning to it. The constant a (2.44) can be written in terms of this coordinate.

$$a = \frac{dx_5}{d\tau} = \sqrt{(\gamma_{55})}\, c \tag{2.53}$$

and thus the identification of the geodesic with the path of a charged particle requires

$$a\alpha = \sqrt{(\gamma_{55})}\,c\alpha = q/M_0 c;$$

q, as already stated, being in electrostatic units. The constant α will be regarded as a fundamental constant not depending on the particular particle under consideration, that is to say, independent of the charge q or the mass M_0.

Suppose that the fundamental unit of electric charge is denoted by e ($-e$ is the charge of the electron). The charge q can be denoted by $n'e$, where n' is an integer, positive or negative, or it may have the value zero.

Suppose that the rest mass of the electron is denoted be m_0. The mass M_0 can be denoted by nm_0, but n is not necessarily integral. Thus

$$\sqrt{(\gamma_{55})}\,c\alpha = n'e/nm_0 c,$$

and if α is to be a fundamental constant independent of the particle, i.e. independent of n' and n, the suggestion from this relation is that

$$\alpha = e/m_0 c^2, \quad \gamma_{55} = (n'/n)^2. \qquad (2.54)$$

The fact that γ_{55} is related to n' and n in this way implies that in the system in which a particle is located the ratio of the number of units of charge to the number of units of mass must be taken into account.

The covariant coefficients (γ_{m5}) are now given by

$$\gamma_{m5} = \gamma_{5m} = \gamma_{55}\,\alpha\phi_m \qquad (2.55)$$

and since the electromagnetic potential is a four-vector, these coefficients also form a four-vector.

In the notation of the tensor calculus

$$\gamma^\mu{}_\nu = \gamma^{\mu\alpha}\gamma_{\nu\alpha} = \delta^\mu{}_\nu \qquad (2.56)$$

where $\delta^\mu{}_\nu$ is the Kronecker delta with the value zero when the affixes are unequal and the value unity when they are equal.

From this it follows that

$$\gamma^m{}_5 = \gamma^{m\nu}\gamma_{5\nu} = \gamma^{mn}\gamma_{5n} + \gamma^{m5}\gamma_{55} = 0$$

and thus

$$\gamma^{m5} = -\frac{\gamma^{mn}\gamma_{5n}}{\gamma_{55}} = -\alpha g^{mn}\phi_n = -\alpha\phi^m. \qquad (2.57)$$

In a similar way, from $\gamma_5{}^5 = \gamma_{5\mu}\gamma^{5\mu} = 1$, it follows that

$$\gamma^{55} = \frac{1}{\gamma_{55}} + \alpha^2 \phi_m \phi^m. \tag{2.58}$$

From these results and also from the relations (2.12) and (2.15) the following table of values of the coefficients can be drawn up:

$$\left.\begin{array}{l} \gamma^{mn} = g^{mn}, \quad \gamma^{m5} = \gamma^{5m} = -\alpha\phi^m, \quad \gamma^{55} = \dfrac{1}{\gamma_{55}} + \alpha^2 \phi_m \phi^m, \\[2mm] \gamma_{mn} = g_{mn} + \gamma_{55}\,\alpha^2 \phi_m \phi_n, \quad \gamma_{m5} = \gamma_{5m} = \gamma_{55}\,\alpha\phi_m, \quad \gamma_{55} = (n'/n)^2 \end{array}\right\} \tag{2.59}$$

The reason for the identification of a four-dimensional scalar $a_.$ with the quantity $A_5/\sqrt(\gamma_{55})$ (cf. 2.17) instead of placing A_5, which transforms like a scalar equal to $a_.$, can be appreciated from the relation (2.52) in which the scalar $cd\tau$ is equated to $dx_5/\sqrt(\gamma_{55})$. This is regarded as a suggestion of how the covariant component of a five-dimensional covariant vector should be related to a four-dimensional scalar quantity, in this case $cd\tau$.

The relations between four- and five-dimensional quantities given in equations (2.17)–(2.25), together with others, can now be tabulated conveniently as follows:

$$\left.\begin{array}{l} A^m = a^m, \quad A_5 = \sqrt(\gamma_{55})\,a_., \\[2mm] A_m = a_m + \sqrt(\gamma_{55})\,\alpha\phi_m a_., \quad A^5 = \dfrac{a_.}{\sqrt(\gamma_{55})} - \alpha\phi_n a^n. \end{array}\right\} \tag{2.60}$$

$$\left.\begin{array}{l} A^{mn} = a^{mn}, \quad A^m{}_5 = \sqrt(\gamma_{55})\,a^m{}_., \quad A_{55} = \gamma_{55}a_{..}, \\[2mm] A^m{}_n = a^m{}_n + \sqrt(\gamma_{55})\,\alpha\phi_n a^m{}_., \quad A^{m5} = \dfrac{a^m{}_.}{\sqrt(\gamma_{55})} - \alpha\phi_n a^{mn}, \\[2mm] A_m{}^5 = \dfrac{a_{m.}}{\sqrt(\gamma_{55})} - \alpha\phi_n a_m{}^n + \alpha\phi_m a_{..} - \sqrt(\gamma_{55})\,\alpha^2 \phi_m \phi_n a_.{}^n, \\[2mm] A_{mn} = a_{mn} + \sqrt(\gamma_{55})\,\alpha\phi_m a_{.n} + \sqrt(\gamma_{55})\,\alpha\phi_n a_{m.} + \gamma_{55}\,\alpha^2 \phi_m \phi_n a_{..}, \\[2mm] A^{55} = \dfrac{a_{..}}{\gamma_{55}} - \alpha\phi_m \dfrac{a^m{}_.}{\sqrt(\gamma_{55})} - \alpha\phi_m \dfrac{a_.{}^m}{\sqrt(\gamma_{55})} + \alpha^2 \phi_m \phi_n a^{mn}, \\[2mm] A_{m5} = \sqrt(\gamma_{55})\,a_{m.} + \alpha\phi_m a_{..}, \quad A_{5m} = \sqrt(\gamma_{55})\,a_{.m} + \alpha\phi_m a_{..} \end{array}\right\} \tag{2.61}$$

Relations of this kind of particular interest occur in association with the operators grad and curl. Suppose that a function V is of the form

$$V = e^{ikx^5} U, \tag{2.62}$$

where U is a function of the four coordinates (x^m) but does not contain x^5.

The gradient of V is the covariant vector (A_μ) with $A_\mu = \partial V/\partial x^\mu$, so that

$$A_m = \frac{\partial V}{\partial x^m}, \quad A_5 = ikV. \tag{2.63}$$

The counterpart of this vector in four dimensions (cf. 2.60) is thus

$$a_m = \left(\frac{\partial}{\partial x^m} - i\alpha k\phi_m\right)V, \quad a_. = \frac{ik}{\sqrt{(\gamma_{55})}}V. \tag{2.64}$$

The components of the curl of a five-vector (F_μ) are

$$A_{\mu\nu} = \frac{\partial F_\nu}{\partial x^\mu} - \frac{\partial F_\mu}{\partial x^\nu}, \tag{2.65}$$

and if for simplicity F_5 is zero,

$$A_{5m} = ikF_m, \tag{2.66}$$

dependence upon x^5 being in accordance with the relation

$$F_m = e^{ikx^5}U_m,$$

U_m being independent of x^5. The vector (F_μ) is related to a four-vector f_m in accordance with the relations (2.60)

$$F_m = f_m + \alpha\phi_m F_5 = f_m.$$

Thus

$$A_{5m} = ikf_m \quad \text{or} \quad \sqrt{(\gamma_{55})}\, a_{.m} = ikf_m$$

and since $A_{55} = \gamma_{55}a_{..} = 0$, it follows from one of the relations (2.61) that

$$A_{mn} = a_{mn} + \alpha\phi_m ikf_n - \alpha\phi_n ikf_m$$

$$a_{mn} = \left(\frac{\partial}{\partial x^m} - ik\alpha\phi_m\right)f_n - \left(\frac{\partial}{\partial x^n} - ik\alpha\phi_n\right)f_m. \tag{2.67}$$

This component is the four-dimensional counterpart of the five-dimensional component of the curl of a vector.

The case of the momentum vector is interesting on account of the importance of its application in quantum mechanics. If M_0 is the rest mass of a particle associated with a charge q, which are written as nm_0 and $n'e$ respectively, the five-dimensional component of momentum is

$$P_m = M_0\gamma_{m\nu}\frac{dx^\nu}{d\tau} = M_0\gamma_{mn}\frac{dx^n}{d\tau} + M_0\gamma_{m5}\frac{dx^5}{d\tau}.$$

33

By means of the relations (2.59) this can be put into the form:

$$P_m = M_0 g_{mn} \frac{dx^n}{d\tau} + \frac{n' e}{c} \phi_m. \tag{2.68}$$

The first term on the right is the four-dimensional component of momentum.

In the classical theory the right-hand side would appear as

$$\left(m\dot{x} + \frac{n' e}{c} \phi_x \right)$$

for the x-component. If

$$P_x = m\dot{x} + \frac{n' e}{c} \phi_x$$

with similar representations for P_y and P_z, in the Lagrange theory of the motion of a charged particle in an electromagnetic field, the components of momentum are not the conjugates of the coordinates. The conjugates are P_x, P_y, P_z and x, y, z, so that from the equation (2.68) it appears that the five-dimensional components of momentum and the coordinates are conjugate.

In quantum mechanics the components of momentum are replaced by the operators $(h/2\pi i)(\partial/\partial x)$, etc., when there is no electromagnetic field, but the essential point is that these operators replace the conjugates of the coordinates and this means that they replace the five-dimensional components of momentum. Thus, from equation (2.68) the four-dimensional component of momentum (p_m) is replaced by

$$p_m = \frac{h}{2\pi i} \cdot \frac{\partial}{\partial x^m} - \frac{n' e}{c} \phi_m. \tag{2.69}$$

If this equation be compared with the first of the relations (2.64) it appears to be a particular case in which

$$\frac{h}{2\pi i} \cdot a_m = p_m V.$$

Thus

$$p_m = \frac{h}{2\pi i} \cdot \frac{\partial}{\partial x^m} - \frac{h\alpha k}{2\pi} \phi_m \tag{2.70}$$

and therefore

$$\frac{h\alpha k}{2\pi} = \frac{n' e}{c}.$$

If the value $\alpha = e/m_0 c^2$ (2.54) be substituted it is seen that

$$k = 2\pi n' m_0 c/h. \tag{2.71}$$

The length $h/m_0 c$ is a fundamental length usually known as the Compton wavelength. It will be denoted by l_0 and the value of k will be assumed to be $2\pi n'/l_0$ throughout the present work. It thus appears that k is an integral multiple of a universal constant and that the coordinate x^5 occurs in the factor $e^{2\pi n' x^5/l_0}$.

The Christoffel bracket expressions and the curvature tensor

The values of the bracket expressions $\Delta^\mu{}_{\rho\sigma}$ and $\Delta_{\rho\sigma\mu}$ already mentioned in the introduction of parallel displacement must now be derived.

They are defined as follows:

$$\Delta^\mu{}_{\rho\sigma} = \tfrac{1}{2}\gamma^{\mu\lambda}\Delta_{\rho\sigma\lambda} = \tfrac{1}{2}\gamma^{\mu\lambda}\left(\frac{\partial\gamma_{\lambda\rho}}{\partial x^\sigma}+\frac{\partial\gamma_{\lambda\sigma}}{\partial x^\rho}-\frac{\partial\gamma_{\rho\sigma}}{\partial x^\lambda}\right). \tag{2.72}$$

The corresponding expressions in four dimensions, to which they are related, are denoted and defined by

$$\Gamma^m_{rs} = g^{ml}\Gamma_{rsl} = \tfrac{1}{2}g^{ml}\left(\frac{\partial g_{lr}}{\partial x^s}+\frac{\partial g_{ls}}{\partial x^r}-\frac{\partial g_{rs}}{\partial x^l}\right). \tag{2.73}$$

Some of the expressions $(\Delta^\mu{}_{\rho\sigma})$ are simplified by the assumption that none of the coefficients $(\gamma_{\mu\nu})$ contain x^5. These are considered first.

(i) $\Delta^\mu{}_{55}$

This vanishes from the definition (2.72) since $\sigma=\rho=5$ and γ_{55} is constant. Thus

$$\Delta^\mu{}_{55} = 0 \tag{2.74}$$

In the case of $\Delta^\mu{}_{\rho5}$ it is necessary to consider separately the cases (ii) $\Delta^m{}_{r5}$ and (iii) $\Delta^5{}_{r5}$.

(ii) $\Delta^m{}_{r5} = \tfrac{1}{2}\gamma^{m\lambda}\left(\frac{\partial\gamma_{\lambda r}}{\partial x^5}+\frac{\partial\gamma_{\lambda5}}{\partial x^r}-\frac{\partial\gamma_{r5}}{\partial x^\lambda}\right) = \tfrac{1}{2}\gamma^{ml}\left(\frac{\partial\gamma_{l5}}{\partial x^r}-\frac{\partial\gamma_{r5}}{\partial x^l}\right)$

since $\gamma_{\lambda r}$ and γ_{r5} are independent of x^5. Thus

$$\Delta^m{}_{r5} = \tfrac{1}{2}\gamma_{55}\,\alpha g^{ml}\left(\frac{\partial\phi_l}{\partial x^r}-\frac{\partial\phi_r}{\partial x^l}\right).$$

In the notation of the electromagnetic theory, where the expression

35

in the brackets is denoted by B_{rl}, a component of electromagnetic induction,

$$\Delta^m_{r5} = \tfrac{1}{2}\gamma_{55}\,\alpha B_r{}^m. \tag{2.75}$$

(iii) In a similar way, it can be shown that

$$\Delta^5_{r5} = -\frac{\gamma_{55}\,\alpha^2}{2}\,\phi^l B_{rl} = -\frac{\gamma_{55}\,\alpha^2}{2}\,\phi_l B_r\,. \tag{2.76}$$

(iv) $\quad \Delta^5_{rs} = -\alpha\phi^l\,\Gamma_{rs,\,l} - \tfrac{1}{2}\gamma_{55}\,\alpha^3\,\phi^l(\phi_r B_{sl} + \phi_s B_{rl}) + \tfrac{1}{2}\alpha\left(\dfrac{\partial\phi_r}{\partial x^s} + \dfrac{\partial\phi_s}{\partial x^r}\right)$

$$= -\tfrac{1}{2}\alpha\phi_l\,\Gamma^l_{rs} - \gamma_{55}\,\alpha^3\,\phi^l(\phi_r B_{sl} + \phi_s B_{rl}) + \tfrac{1}{2}\alpha\left(\frac{\partial\phi_r}{\partial x^s} + \frac{\partial\phi_s}{\partial x^r}\right). \tag{2.77}$$

(v) $$\Delta^p_{rs} = \Gamma^p_{rs} + \tfrac{1}{2}\gamma_{55}\,\alpha^2(\phi_r B_s{}^p + \phi_s B_r{}^p). \tag{2.78}$$

The Riemann–Christoffel tensor, which occurred in the discussion on parallel displacement (1.14) has components of the form:

$$P^\mu_{\lambda\sigma\rho} = \frac{\partial\Delta^\mu_{\lambda\rho}}{\partial x^\sigma} - \frac{\partial\Delta^\mu_{\lambda\sigma}}{\partial x^\rho} + \Delta^\mu_{\nu\sigma}\Delta^\nu_{\lambda\rho} - \Delta^\mu_{\nu\rho}\Delta^\nu_{\lambda\sigma}. \tag{2.79}$$

The curvature tensor $(P_{\lambda\sigma})$, the reduced form of $(B^\mu_{\lambda\sigma\rho})$ plays an important part in the theory of relativity. It is given by

$$P_{\lambda\sigma} = P^\mu_{\lambda\sigma\mu}. \tag{2.80}$$

The corresponding four-dimensional quantities will be denoted by R^m_{lsr} and R_{ls}, and the relations between the four- and five-dimensional components in the case of the curvature tensor will be given.

From (2.79) and (2.80),

$$P_{\lambda\sigma} = \frac{\partial\Delta^\rho_{\lambda\rho}}{\partial x^\sigma} - \frac{\partial\Delta^\rho_{\lambda\sigma}}{\partial x^\rho} + \Delta^\rho_{\nu\sigma}\Delta^\nu_{\lambda\rho} - \Delta^\rho_{\nu\rho}\Delta^\nu_{\lambda\sigma}. \tag{2.81}$$

The simplest component is P_{55}, and on account of the fact that the coefficients $(\gamma_{\mu\nu})$ are independent of x^5 and that Δ^ν_{55} vanishes,

$$P_{55} = \Delta^\rho_{\nu5}\Delta^\nu_{5\rho} = \Delta^r_{n5}\Delta^n_{5r}$$
$$= (\tfrac{1}{2}\gamma_{55}\,\alpha)^2 B_n{}^r B_r{}^n = (\tfrac{1}{2}\gamma_{55}\,\alpha)^2 B_{nr}B^{rn}. \tag{2.82}$$

It is convenient to write

$$B_{nr}B^{nr} = B \tag{2.83}$$

so that

$$P_{55} = -(\tfrac{1}{2}\gamma_{55}\,\alpha)^2 B, \tag{2.84}$$

since $B_{nr} = -B_{rn}$.

Keeping in mind the same limitations to the dependence on x^5, it can be shown that

$$P_{15} = -\tfrac{1}{2}\gamma_{55}\,\alpha\left(\frac{\partial B_l^r}{\partial x^r} - \Gamma_{lr}^n B_n^{\;r} + \Gamma_{nr}^r B_l^{\;n}\right) - \tfrac{1}{4}\gamma_{55}^2\,\alpha^3\,\phi_l B. \quad (2.85)$$

The expression in the brackets is the four-dimensional divergence of the tensor (B_l^r) and can be written in the form:

$$\frac{1}{\sqrt{(-g)}}\frac{\partial(\sqrt{(-g)}\,B_l^r)}{\partial x^r} - \Gamma_{lr}^n B_n^r$$

where g is the determinant $|g_{mn}|$, formed of the coefficients of the line element. In the general theory of relativity it is generally assumed that g has a finite negative value. This is a limitation on the choice of coordinates. The limitation is made definite by assuming that the value of g is unity. This gives rise to considerable simplification in the equations expressing physical laws and is justified by the results.

It can be shown that with the values adopted for the coefficients $(\gamma_{\mu\nu})$ the same assumption can be made for the determinant

$$\gamma = |\gamma_{\mu\nu}|,$$

and this will be adopted in the present work.

The quantity in brackets in equation (2.85) will be denoted by F_l,

$$F_l = \frac{\partial B_l^r}{\partial x^r} - \Gamma_{lr}^n B_n^{\;r} + \Gamma_{nr}^r B_l^{\;n}$$

and associated with this:

$$F^l = \frac{\partial B^{lr}}{\partial x^r} + \Gamma_{nr}^l B^{nr} + \Gamma_{nr}^r B^{ln}.$$

Since Γ_{nr}^l is symmetric in n and r and B^{nr} antisymmetric in these suffixes, it follows that

$$F^l = \frac{1}{\sqrt{(g)}}\frac{\partial}{\partial x^r}(\sqrt{(g)}\,B^{lr}). \quad (2.86)$$

Thus

$$P_{15} = -\tfrac{1}{2}\gamma_{55}\,\alpha F_l - \tfrac{1}{4}\gamma_{55}^2\,\alpha^3\,\phi_l B \quad (2.87)$$

$$P_5^{\;l} = \gamma^{l\mu}P_{5\mu} = \gamma^{lm}P_{5m} + \gamma^{l5}P_{55},$$

and on substitution from equations (2.84) and (2.86) it follows that

$$P_5^{\;l} = -\tfrac{1}{2}\gamma_{55}\,\alpha F^l. \quad (2.88)$$

By means of equations (2.55), (2.84) and (2.86) it can be shown that

$$P_5{}^5 = \tfrac{1}{2}\gamma_{55}\,\alpha^2(\phi^m F_m - \tfrac{1}{2}B), \qquad (2.89)$$

and in a similar way that

$$P_{5l} = -\tfrac{1}{2}\gamma_{55}\,\alpha(F_l + \tfrac{1}{2}\gamma_{55}\,\alpha^2\phi_l B). \qquad (2.90)$$

By means of the equations (2.75)–(2.78) and (2.86) it can be shown that

$$P^{ik} = \gamma^{i\mu}\gamma^{k\nu}P_{\mu\nu} = R^{ik} + \tfrac{1}{2}\gamma_{55}\,\alpha^2 B^{im}B^k{}_m, \qquad (2.91)$$

where R^{ik} is a component of the four-dimensional curvature tensor

$$R^{ik} = g^{im}g^{kn}\left(\frac{\partial\Gamma^r_{mr}}{\partial x^n} - \frac{\partial\Gamma^r_{mn}}{\partial x^r} + \Gamma^l_{mr}\Gamma^r_{nl} - \Gamma^l_{lr}\Gamma^r_{mn}\right). \qquad (2.92)$$

It is to be noted from the relation (2.91) that R^{ik} is not the four-dimensional counterpart of P^{ik}.

The expression for P_{ik} can be obtained from

$$P_{ik} = \gamma_{i\mu}\gamma_{k\nu}P^{\mu\nu} = g_{ip}g_{kl}P^{pl} + g_{kp}\alpha\phi_i P_5{}^p + g_{ip}\alpha\phi_k P^p{}_5 + \alpha^2\phi_i\phi_k P_{55}$$

and by substitution for the components P^{pl}, etc., from the relations given above. The result is

$$P_{ik} = R_{ik} + \tfrac{1}{2}\gamma_{55}\,\alpha^2 B_i{}^m B_{km} - \tfrac{1}{2}\gamma_{55}\,\alpha^2(\phi_i F_k + \phi_k F_i)$$
$$- (\tfrac{1}{2}\gamma_{55}\,\alpha^2)^2\,\phi_i\phi_k B. \qquad (2.93)$$

The following relations can also be obtained

$$P^{5i} = -\tfrac{1}{2}\alpha F^i - \alpha\phi_l R^{li} - \tfrac{1}{2}\gamma_{55}\,\alpha^3\phi_l B^{lm}B^i{}_m \qquad (2.94)$$

$$P^i{}_k = R^i{}_k + \tfrac{1}{2}\gamma_{55}\,\alpha^2 B^{il}B_{kl} - \tfrac{1}{2}\gamma_{55}\,\alpha^2 F^i\phi_k. \qquad (2.95)$$

The expression for the curvature is

$$P = \gamma^{\mu\nu}P_{\mu\nu} \qquad (2.96)$$

and it may be shown that

$$P = R + \tfrac{1}{4}\gamma_{55}\,\alpha^2 B, \qquad (2.97)$$

R denoting the four-dimensional curvature $g^{mn}R_{mn}$. In a four-dimensional continuum the curvature R is unaffected by the presence of an electromagnetic field, but a contribution is made to the five-dimensional curvature P by this field in accordance with equation (2.97).

The law of gravitation and electromagnetism

The law of gravitation first introduced by Einstein [5] as

$$R^{ik} - \tfrac{1}{2} g^{ik} R = 0 \qquad (2.98)$$

suggests the adoption of a wider law of the form

$$P^{\mu\nu} - \tfrac{1}{2} \gamma^{\mu\nu} P = 0. \qquad (2.99)$$

In the case when μ and ν are placed equal to i and k respectively, the relation, according to (2.91) and (2.97), becomes

$$R^{ik} - \tfrac{1}{2} g^{ik} R = \tfrac{1}{2} \gamma_{55} \, \alpha^2 (\tfrac{1}{4} g^{ik} B - B^{im} B^k{}_m). \qquad (2.100)$$

This is the equation expressing the law of gravitation in the absence of matter but when an electromagnetic field exists. The value of the coefficient $\tfrac{1}{2} \gamma_{55} \alpha^2$ differs, however, from that assumed in Einstein's theory, where the value is taken to be $-8\pi K/c^4$, K denoting the Newtonian constant of gravitation and c the velocity of light.

According to the foregoing considerations the coefficient has the value

$$\frac{1}{2} \left(\frac{n'}{n} \right)^2 \frac{e^2}{m \cdot {}^2 c^4},$$

e denoting the fundamental unit of electric charge, and m_0 the mass of the electron. The occurrence of n' and n requires consideration.

It has been stated that emphasis must be placed upon the fact that the concern in physics is with location and not with the nature of the geometry of space. The introduction of the relation $\gamma_{55} = (n'/n)^2$ means that in the location of a particle, the nature of the particle itself must be considered. n' is the integral number of elementary units of charge and nm_0 is the mass of the particle expressed as a multiple of electron rest mass units m_0.

Equation (2.100) indicates that, if at any point there is no charge ($\gamma_{55} = n'^2/n^2$, $n' = 0$), the right-hand side is zero, but that, if there is a charge at the point, there is a local modification of the purely gravitational case.

A property of the tensor $(P^{\mu\nu} - \tfrac{1}{2} \gamma^{\mu\nu} P)$ [6]

In the theory of relativity the tensor $(R^{mn} - \tfrac{1}{2} g^{mn} R)$ is shown to have the property that its divergence vanishes identically. It is this property which causes the tensor to occupy an important place in a physical theory. This can be illustrated by comparison with the case of the current vector (J^m) with components (ρu^m), where ρ is the density of electric charge and $u^m (= dx^m/dt)$ a component of velocity. In this case the vanishing of the divergence is expressed by

$$\frac{\partial J^m}{\partial u^m} = 0$$

or by

$$\frac{\partial}{\partial x}(\rho u_x) + \frac{\partial}{\partial y}(\rho u_y) + \frac{\partial}{\partial z}(\rho u_z) + \frac{\partial \rho}{\partial t} = 0$$

which is the expression of the conservation of electric charge.

If the tensor $(R^{mn} - \frac{1}{2}g^{mn}R)$ is denoted by S^{mn}, the vanishing of the divergence is expressed by

$$\frac{\partial S^{mn}}{\partial x^n} + \Gamma^m_{ln}S^{ln} + \Gamma^n_{lm}S^{ml} = 0. \tag{2.101}$$

To demonstrate this by the substitution of S^{mn} in terms of its dependence on the coefficients (Γ^m_{ln}) is long and tedious, but this can be avoided by noting that the relations concerned are tensor relations so that a special coordinate system may be chosen. If the relation can be shown to hold for this system, it holds generally.

The case of the component $(P^\mu{}_5 - \frac{1}{2}\gamma^\mu{}_5 P)$ is of particular interest in the five-dimensional theory and will serve as an illustration of the property. If it be denoted by $S^\mu{}_5$ it has to be verified that

$$\frac{\partial S^\mu{}_5}{\partial x^\mu} + \Delta^\mu_{\nu\mu}S^\nu{}_5 - \Delta^\nu_{5\mu}S^\mu{}_\nu = 0. \tag{2.102}$$

$S^\mu{}_5$ depends on the coefficients $(\gamma_{\mu\nu})$ and their derivatives so that it is independent of the coordinate x^5. Thus the first term is equal to $\partial S^m{}_5/\partial x^m$ $(m \neq 5)$.

By making use of the relations (2.74)–(2.76) the expression becomes:

$$\frac{\partial S^m{}_5}{\partial x^m} + \Delta^m_{nm}S^n{}_5 - \Delta^n_{5m}S^m{}_n = 0. \tag{2.103}$$

Since $\gamma^m{}_5 = 0$, $S^m{}_5$ may be replaced by $P^m{}_5$ and the third term

$$\Delta^n_{5m}S^m{}_n = \Delta^n_{5m}(P^m{}_n - \frac{1}{2}\gamma^m{}_n P).$$

But by the relation (2.75) $\Delta^n_{5m}\gamma^m{}_n = \frac{1}{2}\gamma_{55}\alpha B_m{}^m$ and since B_{mn} is a component of an antisymmetric tensor $B_m{}^m$ vanishes. Thus the expression now becomes

$$\frac{\partial P^m{}_5}{\partial x^m} + \Delta^m_{nm} P^n{}_5 - \Delta^n_{5m} P^m{}_n = 0. \qquad (2.104)$$

The further reduction of this equation requires the relations (2.74–2.78) and some of those following (2.80). It is helpful to note that the expression $B_{mn} R^{mn}$ vanishes because of the antisymmetry of (B_{mn}) and the symmetry of (R^{mn}), and also to note that the expression $B_m{}^n B^{ml} B_{nl}$ vanishes. This can be seen from the fact that $B_m{}^n B^{ml}$ is symmetrical in n and l while B_{nl} is antisymmetrical.

The equation becomes finally

$$-\tfrac{1}{2}\gamma_{55}\alpha \left(\frac{\partial F^m}{\partial x^m} + \Gamma^m_{nm} F^n \right) = -\tfrac{1}{2}\gamma_{55}\,\alpha\,\mathrm{div}\,F = 0$$

On referring to the relation (2.86), remembering that

$$\mathrm{div}\,F = \frac{1}{\sqrt{(g)}} \frac{\partial}{\partial x^m} [\sqrt{(g)}\,F^m],$$

it appears that

$$\mathrm{div}\,F = \frac{1}{\sqrt{(g)}} \frac{\partial^2}{\partial x^m \partial x^r} [\sqrt{(g)}\,B^{mr}] \qquad (2.105)$$
$$= 0,$$

on account of the antisymmetry of (B^{mr}).

Thus the vanishing of the divergence of the tensor $(P^\mu{}_\nu - \tfrac{1}{2}\gamma^\mu{}_\nu P)$ is verified in the case $\nu = 5$, and in the course of the proof it appears that the four-vector (F^l) is also conserved.

The law of gravitation and of electromagnetism in the presence of matter and of electric charges

In the case of gravitation alone Einstein's law is stated in the form:

$$R^{mn} - \tfrac{1}{2}g^{mn} R = \chi T^{mn}. \qquad (2.106)$$

From the consideration that the divergence of the tensor represented on the left-hand side vanishes it follows that the divergence of the tensor (T^{mn}) must also vanish. This tensor is known as the energy tensor of matter and has the form:

$$T^{mn} = \rho_0 \frac{dx^m}{d\tau} \frac{dx^n}{d\tau}, \qquad (2.107)$$

where ρ_0 denotes the proper density of matter and τ the proper time.

In interpreting this expression in Galilean coordinates, that is to say in expressing it in the familiar form, the ordinary density ρ replaces $\rho_0(dt/d\tau)^2$, t denoting the ordinary time. If the velocity components of the matter are denoted by (u_x, u_y, u_z), then

$$u_x = \frac{dx^1}{dt}, \quad u_y = \frac{dx^2}{dt}, \quad u_z = \frac{dx^3}{dt},$$

and the fourth component $u_4 = dx^4/dt = ic$, since in these coordinates $x^4 = ict$.

Thus the component of (T^{mn}) can be arranged in the form:

$$|T^{mn}| = \begin{matrix} \rho u_x^2 & \rho u_x u_y & \rho u_x u_z & i\rho c u_x \\ \rho u_y u_x & \rho u_y^2 & \rho u_y u_z & i\rho c u_y \\ \rho u_z u_x & \rho u_z u_y & \rho u_z^2 & i\rho c u_z \\ i\rho c u_x & i\rho c u_y & i\rho c u_z & -\rho c^2 \end{matrix}$$

If matter is considered as a collection of small particles in random motion the expression for (T^{mn}) can be obtained in terms of the motion of the centre of mass and the motions relative to it.

In this case the pressure components occur and the terms in the first three lines and columns take the forms of which $(\rho u_y u_z + p_{yz})$ is typical while the fourth line and column are unaltered. In this case the vanishing of the divergence gives the hydrodynamical equations of a fluid, including the equation which expresses the continuity of matter, viz.:

$$\frac{\partial(\rho u_x)}{\partial x} + \frac{\partial(\rho u_y)}{\partial y} + \frac{\partial(\rho u_z)}{\partial z} + \frac{\partial \rho}{\partial t} = 0. \tag{2.108}$$

In the present case the appropriate form of the energy tensor for matter and electricity is at once suggested. The form remains the same, equation (2.81) becomes

$$T^{\mu\nu} = \rho_0 \frac{dx^\mu}{d\tau} \frac{dx^\nu}{d\tau}, \tag{2.109}$$

summation now occurring for $(\mu, \nu) = 1, 2, 3, 4, 5$.

The law corresponding to the law of gravitation becomes

$$P^{\mu\nu} - \tfrac{1}{2}\gamma^{\mu\nu}P = \chi T^{\mu\nu}. \tag{2.110}$$

It should be borne in mind that the constant χ need not, on the principle of covariance in four dimensions, be the same for the four-dimensional tensor, vector and scalar parts of this equation.

For the tensor relation it is convenient to consider equation (2.110) in its contravariant form with $(\mu, \nu) = (m, n)$ and for the vector relation, the mixed form with the lower suffix equal to 5, since by these means it is possible to pass directly to four-dimensional relationships. Thus

$$P^{mn} - \tfrac{1}{2}\gamma^{mn}P = \chi T^{mn}.$$

According to equations (2.99) and (2.100) this becomes

$$R^{mn} - \tfrac{1}{2}g^{mn}R = \tfrac{1}{2}\gamma_{55}\,\alpha^2(\tfrac{1}{4}g^{mn}B - B^{ml}B^n{}_l) + \chi T^{mn}. \quad (2.111)$$

This is the relativistic equation for matter and electricity, but it should be noted that the constants χ and $\tfrac{1}{2}\gamma_{55}\alpha^2$ are not equal as in the general theory of relativity, where χ in this case is placed equal to $-8\pi K/c^4$, K denoting the Newtonian constant.

In the case of the mixed tensor with the lower suffix 5

$$P^m{}_5 - \tfrac{1}{2}\gamma^m{}_5 P = \chi T^m{}_5, \quad (2.112)$$

remembering that χ is not necessarily equal to $-8\pi K/c^4$ in this relation.

Since $m \neq 5$, $\gamma^m{}_5 = 0$ and (2.92) becomes

$$P^m{}_5 = \chi\rho_0 \frac{dx^m}{d\tau}\frac{dx_5}{d\tau}. \quad (2.113)$$

Let there be N particles per unit volume and let the mass of each be nm_0, where m_0 is the electron rest mass. Since

$$\frac{dx_5}{d\tau} = c\sqrt{(\gamma_{55})} = n'c/n,$$

where, as before, n' denotes the number of fundamental changes associated with the particle and n is the number of electron masses associated with it,

$$P^m{}_5 = \chi N n m_0 c\sqrt{(\gamma_{55})}\frac{dx^m}{d\tau} = \chi N n' m_0 c\frac{dx^m}{d\tau}.$$

Thus from equation (2.88)

$$-\tfrac{1}{2}\gamma_{55}\alpha F^m = \chi N n' m_0 c\frac{dx^m}{d\tau}.$$

If χ is given the value $-\frac{1}{2}\gamma_{55}\alpha^2$ in this case,

$$F^m = Nn'm_0c\alpha\frac{dx^m}{d\tau} = Nn'\frac{e}{c}\frac{dx^m}{d\tau} \qquad (2.114)$$

since $\alpha = e/m_0c^2$.

e is measured in electrostatic units, as can be seen from the derivation of the path of a particle from the geodesic, the charge being denoted by q/c electromagnetic units. Thus the term on the right of equation (2.104) is the product of the charge density and the velocity, i.e. the current density vector.

From the definition of (F_m) by equation (2.86) it appears that (2.114) is one of the familiar sets of Maxwell's equations. In order to make this point clear let F_m be written, in accordance with (2.86), with $g = 1$, in the form:

$$\frac{\partial B_m{}^r}{\partial x^r} = F_m = J_m.$$

Neglecting the gravitational field this equation, with $m = 1$ becomes

$$\frac{\partial B_{12}}{\partial x^2} + \frac{\partial B_{13}}{\partial x^3} + \frac{\partial B_{14}}{\partial x^4} = J_1$$

since B_{11} is zero.

The vector potential has the components $(\phi_1, \phi_2, \phi_3, \phi_4)$ and $\phi_4 = i\phi$, where ϕ is the scalar potential. But

$$B_z = \frac{\partial\phi_2}{\partial x^1} - \frac{\partial\phi_1}{\partial x^2} = \frac{\partial\phi_y}{\partial x} - \frac{\partial\phi_x}{\partial y},$$

as usually written and the corresponding expression gives B_y.

$$B_{14} = \frac{\partial\phi_4}{\partial x^1} \quad \frac{\partial\phi_1}{\partial x^4} = i\left(\frac{\partial\phi}{\partial x} + \frac{1}{c}\frac{\partial\phi_1}{\partial t}\right) = -iE_x.$$

Thus

$$\frac{\partial B_z}{\partial y} - \frac{\partial B_y}{\partial z} = \frac{1}{c}\frac{\partial E_x}{\partial t} + J_x$$

which is the x-component of the equation:

$$\operatorname{curl}\mathbf{B} = \frac{1}{c}\frac{\partial\mathbf{E}}{\partial t} + \mathbf{J}.$$

As a result of this presentation of a law of gravitation and electromagnetism by the use of five coordinates a remarkable unity of the laws of conservation of physics is accomplished.

Einstein's law (2.106) leads to the principle of conservation of the total energy and momentum of matter and of the field of gravitation. The law of which equation (2.110) is the expression unites with these the principles of conservation of the energy, and momentum of the electromagnetic field and of electric charge. Thus the vanishing of the divergence of $(P^\mu{}_\nu - \frac{1}{2}\gamma^\mu{}_\nu P)$ in the case $\nu = 5$, leads to

$$\frac{\partial J^m}{\partial x^m} = 0,$$

which is the expression for conservation of charge. It will be noted that this union has been brought about without including any function depending upon the fifth coordinate. All that has been required is the notation of a five-dimensional tensor calculus in which general transformations for four coordinates are allowed but only a very restricted one for the fifth is permitted.

Bibliography

1. TH. KALUZA, 1921. *Sber. preuss. Akad. Wiss.*, 966.
   O. KLEIN, 1927. *Z. Phys.*, **46**, 188.
2. A. EINSTEIN, 1916. *Annln. Phys.* **49**, § 9.
   A. S. EDDINGTON, 1930. *The Mathematical Theory of Relativity*, 2nd edn., § 28.
3. J. W. FISHER, 1929. *Proc. R. Soc. A.*, **123**, 480.
4. L. ROSENFELD, 1927. *Acad. Roy. Belgique*, **XII**, 447.
5. A. EINSTEIN, *loc. cit.*, § 13 *sqq.*
   A. S. EDDINGTON, *loc. cit.*, Chap. III.
6. A. S. EDDINGTON, *loc. cit.*, § 52.
7. A. S. EDDINGTON, *loc. cit.*, § 53.

CHAPTER 3

Field Theories

Field theories will be described in this chapter which have been used in attempts at reaching an explanation and a description of certain problems presented by atomic physics, particularly of those concerning the nucleus.

Although these theories differ from Maxwell's theory of the electromagnetic field they draw upon the ideas and notation contained in, and expressed by, Maxwell's equations. The notation used here is that of the five-dimensional system for it has the merit of being comprehensive, uniting electromagnetic fields automatically with nuclear fields and it introduces by analogy certain necessary quantities, which other methods of description introduce arbitrarily.

Gravitational fields are also automatically united with the other fields, but on account of the relative weakness of gravitational effects in nuclear phenomena and, indeed in most cases of electromagnetic phenomena, they can be neglected. This means that in practice there need be no distinction between four-dimensional covariance and contravariance. Thus in the case of vector components A^m may be replaced by A_m or vice versa and similarly, with tensors, T^{mn} may be replaced by T_{mn}. But in the case when an electromagnetic field exists, care must be taken since the coefficients $(\gamma_{\mu\nu}, \gamma^{\mu\nu})$ will depend on the electromagnetic potential and it is not possible to write $\gamma_{\mu\nu} = \gamma^{\mu\nu}$ or $T_{\mu\nu} = T^{\mu\nu}$.

In nuclear problems, it is sometimes possible to neglect the electromagnetic field on account of the relative magnitude of this field and the nuclear field. In these cases since the potential components vanish,

$$\gamma^{m5} = \gamma_{m5} = 0, \quad \gamma^{mn} = \gamma_{mn},$$

but γ_{55} and γ^{55} do not vanish.

There are two different approaches to field theories. In one emphasis is laid upon the existence of generators of the field as in the case of

46

Lorentz's theory of the electromagnetic field, where the existence of charged particles was assumed, their charge and motion giving rise to the field. The discovery of the electron and the success of the theory strongly supported this view of the nature of the origin of the electromagnetic field. There has, however, always been the difficulty concerning the energy of the field. If the charge is regarded as a point charge the energy of the field is infinitely great. To avoid this difficulty it has been found necessary to introduce a small but finite dimension to the charged particle.

There is no fundamental objection to this in the classical theory of the electron but the dimension introduced has no relation to the theory. It is a concept arbitrarily introduced. This difficulty has been taken over in modern theories of the electric charge and infinite magnitudes have only been avoided by a special hypothesis. Moreover it is difficult to introduce the concept of a finite particle into the quantum theory and, with it, to satisfy the demands of the special theory of relativity.

The other approach to a field theory, associated with the name of Gustav Mie, places the emphasis on the field quantities and leaves aside the question of the existence of a particle.

There are difficulties concerning this point of view in the electromagnetic theory, particularly in respect of the significance attached to the electromagnetic potential, which, in the generally accepted form of the theory, is no more than an auxiliary in the derivation of field intensities, and is, in fact, not unique. But Mie's theory has introduced a new point of view and has been adopted, in some cases apparently inadvertently, in the theory of the nuclear field.

As an introduction to the notation used in field theories reference will be made to the theory of electromagnetism since it is the most familiar field theory of physics and sets the pattern of formulation. It is an example of a vector theory, the field components being derived from the vector potential (ϕ_m). These components are denoted by (B_{mn}) (cf. 2.38) and are derived by the formula:

$$B_{mn} = \frac{\partial \phi_n}{\partial x^m} - \frac{\partial \phi_m}{\partial x^n}.$$ (3.1)

Another tensor characteristic of the field is usually denoted by (H_{mn}).

As already seen in considering the equation of the geodesic, it is often convenient to make use of the relations (2.39) and there are similar relations for the components of (H_{mn}):

$$H_{23} = H_x, \quad H_{31} = H_y, \quad H_{12} = H_z, \left.\vphantom{\begin{array}{c}a\\b\end{array}}\right\} \tag{3.2}$$
$$H_{41} = iD_x, \quad H_{42} = iD_y, \quad H_{43} = iD_z.$$

Components of polarization I and P are introduced in the usual notation as follows:

$$B = H + 4\pi I, \quad E = D + 4\pi P. \tag{3.3}$$

In the present considerations the factor 4π will be omitted and these two relations will be combined in the form

$$F_{mn} = V_{mn} + S_{mn}, \tag{3.4}$$

the letters F, V and S being introduced since the letters B, H, E, D, I and P are so frequently associated with Maxwell's theory but the tensor (V_{mn}) will correspond to the tensor (H_{mn}) of the electromagnetic field, that is to say to **H** and **D** of the electromagnetic theory, (F_{mn}) will correspond to (B_{mn}) or to **B** and **E**, and (S_{mn}) to the polarizations **I** and **P**.

The scalar field theory

In the scalar field in the four-dimensional notation, the field component (F_m) is a vector derived from a scalar quantity, θ, by means of

$$F_m = \frac{\partial \theta}{\partial x^m}. \tag{3.5}$$

In the five-dimensional notation the field components are denoted by (F_μ) and (V_μ) with

$$F_\mu = V_\mu + S_\mu \tag{3.6}$$

and the field equations are:

$$\frac{\partial F_\mu}{\partial x^\nu} - \frac{\partial F_\nu}{\partial x^\mu} = 0 \tag{3.7}$$

and

$$\frac{1}{\sqrt{(\gamma)}} \frac{\partial}{\partial x^\mu} [\sqrt{(\gamma)} \, V^\mu] = 0. \tag{3.8}$$

The latter is equivalent to div $V^\mu=0$ and it is convenient to choose $\gamma=1$, so that

$$\frac{\partial V^\mu}{\partial x^\mu} = 0. \tag{3.9}$$

The dependence of functions upon the coordinate x^5 will still be assumed to be through the factor e^{ikx^5}. They will be of the form $U(x^m)e^{ikx^5}$, where $U(x^m)$ depends upon the four coordinates (x^1, x^2, x^3, x^4).

By analogy with the occurrence in many cases of components of momentum in the factor $\exp(2\pi i P_m x^m/h)$ the suggestion may be made that the factor containing x^5 is $e^{2\pi i \Pi_5 x^5/h}$, h denoting Planck's constant.

$$\Pi_5 = M_0 \gamma_{5\mu} \frac{dx^\mu}{d\tau} = M_0 \frac{dx_5}{d\tau}. \tag{3.10}$$

From equations (2.53) and (2.54) it follows that

$$\Pi_5 = M_0 \sqrt{(\gamma_{55})}\, c = n' m_0 c, \tag{3.11}$$

where n' is an integer denoting the number of fundamental charges, e, associated with the particle of which the mass $M_0=nm_0$, m_0, as usual, being the rest mass of the electron.

Thus the exponential factor is equal to $e^{2\pi i n' x^5/l_0}$ where l_0 is the fundamental length $h/m_0 c$ in agreement with the value of k given in equation (2.71). The four-dimensional counterpart of Π_5 is

$$p_. = \frac{\Pi_5}{\sqrt{(\gamma_{55})}} = nm_0 c = M_0 c \tag{3.11}$$

and it is interesting that while the five-dimensional Π_5 is proportional to the charge of the particle, the four-dimensional $p_.$ is proportional to the mass.

From equation (3.7) with $\nu=5$, it follows that

$$ikF_\mu = \frac{\partial F_5}{\partial x^\mu} \tag{3.12}$$

and F_5/ik is to be identified with the scalar, θ, of equation (3.5).

If F_5 is substituted for the corresponding four-dimensional quantity

$$f_. = \frac{F_5}{\sqrt{(\gamma_{55})}} = \frac{n}{n'} F_5,$$

$$F_m = \frac{1}{ik} \frac{\partial F_5}{\partial x^m} = \frac{h}{2\pi i n m_0 c} \frac{\partial f_.}{\partial x^m}. \tag{3.13}$$

The quantity $2\pi n m_0 c/h$ will be denoted by κ so that

$$F_m = \frac{1}{i\kappa}\frac{\partial f_.}{\partial x^m} = \frac{1}{ik}\frac{\partial F_5}{\partial x^m}. \tag{3.14}$$

These relations associate a particle of rest mass, M_0, with the field and the place of this particle in the field is comparable with that of the photon in the electromagnetic field.

The component F_m is related to the four-dimensional quantity f_m in accordance with equations (2.64). In this case $V = f_./i\kappa$ and $a_m = f_m$, so that

$$M_0 c f_m = \left(\frac{h}{2\pi i}\frac{\partial}{\partial x^m} - \frac{n'e}{c}\phi_m\right)f_.\tag{3.15}$$

In the absence of an electromagnetic field

$$f_m = \frac{1}{i\kappa}\frac{\partial f_.}{\partial x^m}. \tag{3.16}$$

The equation (3.9) can be written in the form

$$\frac{\partial V^m}{\partial x^m} + ik V^5 = 0 \tag{3.17}$$

and by reference to equations (2.17) and (2.21) it can be seen that in terms of four-dimensional quantities the equation becomes:

$$\left(\frac{h}{2\pi i}\frac{\partial}{\partial x^m} - \frac{n'e}{c}\phi_m\right)v^m = -M_0 c v_. \tag{3.18}$$

In the case in which $V^\mu = F^\mu$, corresponding to the absence of polarization in the electromagnetic theory, this equation becomes:

$$\frac{\partial f^m}{\partial x^m} = -i\kappa f. \tag{3.19}$$

and in the absence of a gravitational field $f^m = f_m$ so that the equation for $f_.$ is

$$\sum_m \frac{\partial^2 f_.}{\partial(x_m)^2} = \kappa^2 f_., \tag{3.20}$$

an equation of importance in nuclear field theory. More generally it is not possible to place $V^\mu = F^\mu$, and equations in terms of (V^μ) and (S^μ) are necessary, the former corresponding to components of field intensity and the latter to components of a current vector.

The case will be considered in which the electromagnetic and gravitational fields can be neglected, so that equation (3.16) is applicable.

Thus introducing the four-dimensional quantities v_m, s_m, $v_.$ and $s_.$,

$$v_m + s_m = \frac{1}{i\kappa} \frac{\partial f_.}{\partial x^m}. \tag{3.21}$$

If the suffix k can have the values 1, 2, 3

$$v_k + s_k = \frac{1}{i\kappa} \frac{\partial f_.}{\partial x^k}$$

and the three cases can be expressed together as:

$$\mathbf{V} + \mathbf{S} = \frac{1}{i\kappa} \operatorname{grad} f_.. \tag{3.22}$$

In the case $x = 4$,

$$v_4 + s_4 = \frac{1}{i\kappa} \frac{\partial f_.}{\partial x^4}. \tag{3.23}$$

But it is convenient to introduce differentiation with respect to time and to replace the fourth components of vectors by components in which the system of coordinates is $(x^1, x^2, x^3, x^0 = ct)$. The fourth components of a vector are then denoted by v^0 or v_0 where

$$v^4 = iv^0, \quad v_4 = -iv_0. \tag{3.24}$$

In the absence of a gravitational field $v^4 = v_4$ but $v^0 = -v_0$.

Thus from (3.23)

$$v_0 + s_0 = \frac{1}{i\kappa c} \frac{\partial f_.}{\partial t}. \tag{3.25}$$

Equation (3.7) gives the two relations:

$$\operatorname{curl} \mathbf{V} = -\operatorname{curl} \mathbf{S}, \tag{3.26}$$

and

$$\dot{\mathbf{V}} + \dot{\mathbf{S}} = c \operatorname{grad}(v_0 + s_0). \tag{3.27}$$

Remembering that

$$V^5 = \frac{V_5}{\gamma_{55}} - \alpha \phi_m V^m,$$

51

and that $\phi_m = 0$, V^5 can be replaced by V_5/γ_{55} or $v./\sqrt{(\gamma_{55})}$, then equation (3.17) becomes

$$\frac{\partial v^k}{\partial x^k} + \frac{1}{c}\frac{\partial v^0}{\partial t} = -i\kappa v.,\tag{3.28}$$

or

$$\operatorname{div}\mathbf{V} + \frac{1}{c}\dot{v}^0 = -i\kappa(f. - s.).\tag{3.29}$$

The function θ introduced in equation (3.5) is evidently equal to $f./i\kappa$ and it is convenient sometimes to make use of it. The field equations now become:

$$\left.\begin{aligned}
\mathbf{V} + \mathbf{S} &= \operatorname{grad}\theta \\
v_0 + s_0 &= \frac{1}{c}\dot{\theta} \\
\operatorname{curl}\mathbf{V} &= -\operatorname{curl}\mathbf{S} \\
\dot{\mathbf{V}} + \dot{\mathbf{S}} &= c\operatorname{grad}(v_0 + s_0) \\
\operatorname{div}\mathbf{V} + \frac{1}{c}v^0 &= \operatorname{div}\mathbf{V} - \frac{1}{c}\dot{v}_0 = i\kappa s. + \kappa^2\theta.
\end{aligned}\right\}\tag{3.30}$$

Note on the Lagrange function and the derivation of field equations

The derivation of field equations can proceed from a well-known principle of variation by the adoption of a Lagrange density function L, which depends on certain functions (U) and their first derivatives with respect to the coordinates $(\partial U/\partial x^\mu)$.

The principle of variation consists in the assumption

$$\delta \int L\,d\omega = 0,\tag{3.31}$$

where $d\omega$ is an element of generalized volume, in the present case $d\omega = dx^1 dx^2 dx^3 dx^4 dx^5$, and in this variation the values of the functions (U) are kept constant at the boundaries of the region of integration. It will, moreover, be assumed that the function L does not depend explicitly on the coordinates.

The variation considered is that which results when a function U is changed to a neighbouring function $U + \delta U$ and in cases where L depends upon U and also upon its complex conjugate U^*, it is assumed that the variation of one is independent of that of the other.

From the condition (3.31) the following equation results

$$\frac{\partial}{\partial x^\mu}\frac{\partial L}{\partial\left(\dfrac{\partial U}{\partial x^\mu}\right)}-\frac{\partial L}{\partial U}=0,\tag{3.32}$$

together with similar equations for all the functions U and for their complex conjugates.

An important consequence of this principle is that the tensor with a component $(\Theta^\mu{}_\nu)$ given by

$$\Theta^\mu{}_\nu=\sum\frac{\partial L}{\partial\left(\dfrac{\partial U}{\partial x^\mu}\right)}\frac{\partial U}{\partial x^\nu}-\gamma^\mu{}_\nu L,\tag{3.33}$$

where the summation is made over all the functions (U) and their conjugates, satisfies the condition:

$$\frac{\partial\Theta^\mu{}_\nu}{\partial x^\mu}=0,\tag{3.34}$$

that is to say that the tensor $(\Theta^\mu{}_\nu)$ is conserved.

When L is properly chosen this tensor is the 'energy'-tensor appropriate to all the fields together; gravitational, electromagnetic, nuclear and any others that may exist.

The purpose at present is to consider particularly the nuclear field theories and the gravitational and electromagnetic fields will be neglected. This means that L will not be regarded as depending appreciably upon the coefficients $(\gamma^{\mu\nu})$, which means that it is assumed not to depend on the coefficients (g^{mn}) or upon the electromagnetic vector potential (ϕ_m) and their derivatives.

The function L, will be supposed to depend upon scalar, vector and ultimately also upon spinor quantities in this study of vector fields.

The Hamiltonian function

In the subject of rigid dynamics the Hamiltonian function, H, is a function of the coordinates (q_n) and the components of generalized momentum (p_n). It is defined by the relation

$$H=\sum p_n\dot{q}_n-L,\tag{3.35}$$

5

L being a function of the coordinates (q_n) and their time derivatives $(\dot{q}_n)$.

The Lagrange equations are:

$$\frac{d}{dt}\left(\frac{\partial L}{\partial \dot{q}_n}\right) - \frac{\partial L}{\partial q_n} = 0, \qquad (3.36)$$

for all the coordinates (q_n), and the generalized components of momentum are defined by

$$p_n = \frac{\partial L}{\partial \dot{q}_n}. \qquad (3.37)$$

It follows that

$$dH = \dot{q}_n dp_n - \frac{\partial L}{\partial q_n} dq_n, \qquad (3.38)$$

with summation over n. Thus

$$\dot{q}_n = \frac{\partial H}{\partial p_n}$$

and

$$\frac{\partial H}{\partial q_n} = -\frac{\partial L}{\partial q_n} = -\frac{dp_n}{dt},$$

by equation (3.36). The Hamiltonian function is thus

$$H = \dot{q}_n \frac{\partial L}{\partial \dot{q}_n} - L. \qquad (3.39)$$

In field theories the function L depends on a set of functions of the coordinates and on their differential coefficients with respect to the coordinates, the time being represented by $x^4(=ict)$. Thus the generalized coordinates (q_n) which were regarded as functions of the time are replaced by the functions (U) dependent on all the co-ordinates. In the case in which the functions (U) are the components of a covariant vector (U_μ), it is thus suggested that the Hamiltonian function should take a more general form in which (q_n) is replaced by (U_μ) and (p_n) is replaced by $\partial L/[\partial(\partial U_\mu/\partial x^4)]$. Thus the generalization of equation (3.39) is

$$H = \sum \frac{\partial L}{\partial\left(\dfrac{\partial U_\mu}{\partial x^4}\right)} \frac{\partial U_\mu}{\partial x^4} - L, \qquad (3.40)$$

where the summation is taken over μ and also over all the functions (U_μ) and their complex conjugates $(U_\mu{}^*)$.

Thus, referring to equation (3.33), the function H is seen to be equivalent to the component $\Theta^4{}_4$ of the energy tensor.

If, in equation (3.35), the function L is taken to be the difference between the kinetic and potential energies expressed as a function of the coordinates and velocity, the function H denotes the total energy. In field theories many writers choose the function L in such a way that the tensor component $\Theta^4{}_4$ has the value of minus the energy density so that the total energy of the field is given by

$$W = -\int H\,dv = -\int \Theta^4{}_4\,dv, \qquad (3.41)$$

dv denoting an element of three-dimensional volume.

The Lagrange function and theory of the scalar field

The density function L for the scalar field is

$$L = \tfrac{1}{2}(F^{*\mu}F_\mu - S^{*\mu}F_\mu - S^\mu F^*{}_\mu). \qquad (3.42)$$

As already assumed, the function F_μ is given by

$$F_\mu = \frac{\partial\theta}{\partial x^\mu}. \qquad (3.43)$$

At this stage nothing will be said of the nature of the functions S^μ and $S^{*\mu}$ except that they are functions of the coordinates but do not depend upon θ or $\partial\theta/\partial x^\mu$. The theory thus remains incomplete until a decision upon the structure of these functions is made. This will result in a later chapter from the derivation of the quantum equation.

The field equations can be derived from the Lagrange equations

$$\frac{\partial}{\partial x^\mu}\frac{\partial L}{\partial\left(\dfrac{\partial\theta}{\partial x^\mu}\right)} - \frac{\partial L}{\partial\theta} = 0 \qquad (3.44)$$

and since in this case L does not depend explicitly upon θ and

$$\frac{\partial L}{\partial\left(\dfrac{\partial\theta}{\partial x^\mu}\right)} = \frac{\partial L}{\partial F_\mu} = \tfrac{1}{2}(F^{*\mu} - S^{*\mu}) = \tfrac{1}{2}V^{*\mu} \qquad (3.45)$$

it follows that

$$\frac{\partial V^{*\mu}}{\partial x^\mu} = 0$$

and in the same way $\partial V^\mu / \partial x^\mu = 0$. The latter has already been quoted (cf. 3.9) and the former is the conjugate equation.

The equation (3.7)

$$\frac{\partial F_\mu}{\partial x^\nu} - \frac{\partial F_\nu}{\partial x^\mu} = 0$$

results from equation (3.43).

The energy tensor (cf. 3.33) is

$$\Theta^\mu_{\ \nu} = \frac{\partial L}{\partial\left(\dfrac{\partial\theta}{\partial x^\mu}\right)}\frac{\partial\theta}{\partial x^\nu} + \frac{\partial L}{\partial\left(\dfrac{\partial\theta^*}{\partial x^\mu}\right)}\frac{\partial\theta^*}{\partial x^\nu} - \gamma^\mu_{\ \nu} L \tag{3.46}$$

remembering that θ and θ^* are to be considered as two functions varying independently in the variational process. Thus

$$\Theta^\mu_{\ \nu} = \tfrac{1}{2}(V^{*\mu} F_\nu + V^\mu F^*_{\ \nu}) - \tfrac{1}{2}\gamma^\mu_{\ \nu}(F^{*\alpha} F_\alpha - S^{*\alpha} F_\alpha - S^\alpha F^*_{\ \alpha}). \tag{3.47}$$

It must, however, be remembered that this is not the complete energy tensor, since the contribution from the variation of $S^{*\mu}$ and S^μ has not yet been taken into account.

The tensor given by equation (3.47) is not conserved for this reason. Later on the definition of $S^{*\mu}$ and S^μ will provide the complete tensor with the property of conservation.

The component

$$\Theta^4_{\ 4} = \tfrac{1}{2}(V^{*4} F_4 + V^4 F^*_{\ 4}) - \tfrac{1}{2}(F^{*\alpha} F_\alpha - S^{*\alpha} F_\alpha - S^\alpha F^*_{\ \alpha}) \tag{3.48}$$

and the energy density is $-\Theta^4_{\ 4}$.

It is worth while to draw attention to a point on the question of notation in relation to these formulae. The usual custom of denoting a quantity by A and its conjugate by A^* is followed except in the cases of a vector or tensor component containing a suffix 4. Thus $A^*_{\ 4}$ is not the conjugate of A_4, although it is convenient to describe it in this way. The reason for this departure from the general rule is because the coordinate x^4 is imaginary and it is not desired to introduce a conjugate component x^{*4}. The real coordinate x^0 is in this respect preferable, $x^0 = ct$ and $x^4 = ix^0$. The reason for retaining x^4 is to preserve the analogy with three-dimensional space, writing

$$ds^2 = (dx^1)^2 + (dx^2)^2 + (dx^3)^2 + (dx^4)^2$$

instead of

$$ds^2 = (dx^{1\,2}) + (dx^2)^2 + (dx^3)^2 - (dx^0)^2.$$

In passing from the system in which a vector with components (A^k, A^0) $(k=1,2,3)$ to one in which the components are (A'^k, A'^4) the transformation is made by the change of coordinates

$$x'^k = x^k, \quad x'^4 = ix^0.$$

It is clear that $A'^k = A^k$, $A'^4 = iA^0$. Thus the vector in the second system may be denoted by (A^k, A^4) with $A^4 = iA^0$.

If a function of the components (A^k, A^0) exists with coordinates (x^k, x^0), its complex conjugate will contain the components (A^{*k}, A^{*0}), these denoting the complex conjugates of (A^k, A^0). In terms of the vector (A^k, A^4), the coordinates being (x^k, x^4), the complex function will contain (A^{*k}, A^{*4}), A^{*4} not now denoting the complex conjugate of A^4, the notation being retained in accordance with common use and for convenience. It is necessary to remember in passing from a function to the conjugate complex quantity that since x_4 is imaginary this modification for vector and tensor components containing the affix 4 is made.

A similar argument can be extended to the covariant components (A_m) and also to tensor components. The following table gives examples of the relations most commonly required:

$$\left. \begin{aligned} A^4 &= iA^0, & A^{*4} &= iA^{*0}, & A_4 &= -iA_0, & A_4{}^* &= -iA_0{}^* \\ A^{k4} &= iA^{k0}, & A^{*k4} &= iA^{*k0}, & A^k{}_4 &= -iA^k{}_0, & A^{*k}{}_4 &= -iA^{*k}{}_0 \\ A^{44} &= -A^{00}, & A^{*44} &= -A^{*00}, & A_{44} &= -A_{00}, & A^*{}_{44} &= -A^*_{00} \\ A_{k4} &= -iA_{k0}, & A^*_{k4} &= -iA^*_{k0}, \end{aligned} \right\}$$

$$(3.49)$$

The values of $\int L\,dv$ and of $\int H\,dv$

In the calculation of the field energy in accordance with equation (3.48) the value of $\int L\,dv$ is required; dv denoting the volume element $dx\,dy\,dz$ or $dx^1\,dx^2\,dx^3$. The expression

$$L = \tfrac{1}{2}(F^{*\mu}F_\mu - S^{*\mu}F_\mu - S^\mu F^*{}_\mu)$$

can be written in the form:

$$L = \tfrac{1}{4}(V^{*\mu}F_\mu - S^{*\mu}F_\mu) + \text{c.c.}, \qquad (3.50)$$

where c.c. denotes the complex conjugate of the quantity which precedes it.

$$\int V^{*\mu}F_\mu\,dv = \frac{1}{ik}\int V^{*\mu}\frac{\partial F_5}{\partial x^\mu}\,dv.$$

If the suffix k has the values 1, 2, 3, the right-hand side can be expressed as

$$\frac{1}{ik} \int \left(V^{*k} \frac{\partial F_5}{\partial x^k} + V^4 \frac{\partial F_5}{\partial x^4} + V^{*5} \frac{\partial F_5}{\partial x^5} \right) dx^1 \, dx^2 \, dx^3.$$

On partial integration of the first term, assuming that F_5 vanishes at the limits of integration, and substituting $\partial F_5/\partial x^5 = ikF_5$, the expression becomes

$$\frac{1}{ik} \int \left\{ \left(ikV^{*5} - \frac{\partial V^{*k}}{\partial x^k} \right) F_5 + V^{*4} \frac{\partial F_5}{\partial x^4} \right\} dv. \tag{3.51}$$

Since the complex conjugate quantity V^{*5} contains the factor $\exp(-ikx^5)$ the first term of the integrand may be written in the form $-\partial V^{*5}/\partial x^5$. According to the field equation (3.9), $\partial V^{*\mu}/\partial x^\mu = 0$, so that the expression (3.51) takes the form:

$$\frac{1}{ik} \int \left(F_5 \frac{\partial V^{*4}}{\partial x^4} + V^{*4} \frac{\partial F_5}{\partial x^4} \right) dv.$$

Thus

$$\int L \, dv = \tfrac{1}{4} \int \left\{ \frac{1}{ik} \left(F_5 \frac{\partial V^{*4}}{\partial x^4} + V^{*4} \frac{\partial F_5}{\partial x^4} \right) - S^{*\mu} F_\mu \right\} dv + \text{c.c.} \tag{3.52}$$

From the equation (3.48)

$$\int H \, dv = \int \Theta^4{}_4 \, dv = \frac{1}{2ik} \int V^{*4} \frac{\partial F_5}{\partial x^4} dv + \text{c.c.} - \int L \, dv$$

$$= \frac{1}{4ik} \int \left(V^{*4} \frac{\partial F_5}{\partial x^4} - F_5 \frac{\partial V^{*4}}{\partial x^4} \right) dv$$

$$+ \tfrac{1}{4} \int S^{*\mu} F_\mu \, dv + \text{c.c.} \tag{3.53}$$

F_4 being replaced by $(1/ik)(\partial F_5/\partial x^4)$.

The expression

$$S^{*\mu} F_\mu = \frac{1}{ik} \left(S^{*k} \frac{\partial F_5}{\partial x^k} + S^{*4} \frac{\partial F_5}{\partial x^4} + ikS^{*5} F_5 \right),$$

and on integrating the first term over the volume, again assuming that F_5 vanishes at the boundary, it is found that

$$\int S^{*\mu} F_\mu \, dv = \frac{1}{ik} \int \left(S^{*4} \frac{\partial F_5}{\partial x^4} - F_5 \frac{\partial S^{*k}}{\partial x^k} \right) dv + \int S^{*5} F_5 \, dv. \tag{3.54}$$

In the application of the scalar field theory to the nuclear field the vector (S^m) appears as a current vector which is conserved. Thus

$$\frac{\partial S^k}{\partial x^k} + \frac{\partial S^4}{\partial x^4} = 0$$

and in the static case, there being no variation with respect to time, $\partial S^4/\partial x^4$ vanishes. Thus in the static case

$$\int H \, dv = \tfrac{1}{4} \int S^{*5} F_5 \, dv + \text{c.c.}$$

$$= \tfrac{1}{4} \int (S^{*5} F_5 + S^5 F^*_5) \, dv.$$

In the absence of an electromagnetic field $S^5 = S_5/\gamma_{55}$ and by equations (2.60) and (2.61)

$$\int H \, dv = \tfrac{1}{4} \int (s^* . f . + s . f^* .) \, dv. \tag{3.55}$$

With these simplifications the differential equation for F_5 or $f.$ takes a simple form.

In the static case the equation, $\partial V^\mu/\partial x^\mu = 0$, becomes

$$\frac{\partial V^k}{\partial x^k} + ik V^5 = 0$$

and since $\partial S^k/\partial x^k$ is assumed to vanish,

$$\frac{\partial F^k}{\partial x^k} + ik V^5 = 0,$$

but in this case of no electromagnetic field

$$V^5 = \frac{V_5}{\gamma_{55}} = \frac{F_5 - S_5}{\gamma_{55}},$$

so that since $F_k = (1/ik)(\partial F_5/\partial x^k)$, and $F^k = F_k$ in the absence of a gravitational field,

$$\frac{1}{ik} \sum_k \frac{\partial^2 F_5}{\partial (x^k)^2} + ik \frac{F_5}{\gamma_{55}} = ik \frac{S_5}{\gamma_{55}}$$

or

$$\sum_k \frac{\partial^2 f.}{\partial (x^k)^2} - \frac{k^2 f.}{\gamma_{55}} = -\frac{k^2 s.}{\gamma_{55}}.$$

Since $k = 2\pi n' m_0 c/h$ and $\gamma_{55} = n'^2/n^2$, the equation can be written as

$$\sum_k \frac{\partial^2 f.}{\partial (x^k)^2} - \kappa^2 f. = -\kappa^2 s. \tag{3.56}$$

with $\kappa = 2\pi n m_0 c/h$.

It thus appears that $f.$ can be determined in terms of $s.$ and from $f.$ the field components can be deduced. The solution of this equation can be obtained by means of Green's theorem, which is usually expressed in the form:

$$\int \left(U \frac{\partial V}{\partial n} - V \frac{\partial U}{\partial n} \right) dS = \int (U\nabla^2 V - V\nabla^2 U)\, dv, \tag{3.57}$$

the integrations being applied to the boundary and volume of a region of which the surface element is dS and the volume element dv. The integration will be applied to two surfaces S_1 and S_2 and to the volume between them. It will be supposed that the contribution to the surface integral over S_2 is zero and the surface S_1 will be taken to be an infinitely small sphere so that the value of U over S_1 can be taken as its value at the centre of the sphere, chosen for convenience as the origin of coordinates.

If $\mathbf{U}$ is placed equal to $f.$ and $\kappa^2 s.$ is placed equal to R,

$$\nabla^2 U - \kappa^2 U = -R.$$

Take
$$V = e^{-\kappa r}/r,$$

then
$$\nabla^2 V = \frac{1}{r^2} \frac{\partial}{\partial r} \left(r^2 \frac{\partial V}{\partial r} \right) = \kappa^2 V.$$

Thus the right-hand side of (3.57) becomes $\int RV\, dv$. On the left-hand side the normals are positive when directed away from the enclosed volume and, since r tends to zero, the only term remaining is $4\pi U_0$, where U_0 is the value of U at the centre of the sphere. Thus

$$U_0 = \frac{1}{4\pi} \int RV\, dv = \frac{1}{4\pi} \int \frac{R\, e^{-\kappa r}}{r}\, dv. \tag{3.58}$$

If a new origin is taken, the old one being then at the end of a vector $\mathbf{r}$, and the vector to an element of volume dv_a being denoted by $\mathbf{r}_a$, (3.58) can be written in the form:

$$U = \frac{1}{4\pi} \int \frac{R_a\, e^{-\kappa(\overline{\mathbf{r} - \mathbf{r}_a})}}{\overline{\mathbf{r} - \mathbf{r}_a}}\, dv_a, \tag{3.59}$$

$(\mathbf{r} - \mathbf{r}_a)$ is the vector from the point at which U is measured to an element of volume dv_a, and $\overline{\mathbf{r} - \mathbf{r}_a}$ is the distance between the point and the element. R_a is the value of R at the element.

For convenience the factor of R_a in the integrand will be denoted by $\phi(r, r_a)$. Thus

$$U = \int R_a \phi(r, r_a) \, dv_a. \tag{3.60}$$

The solution of equation (3.56) is thus

$$f. = \int \kappa^2 s._a \phi(r, r_a) \, dv_a. \tag{3.61}$$

Thus the energy associated with this field is

$$W = -\int H \, dv = -\frac{\kappa^2}{4} \iint (s^*. s._a + s. s^*.) \phi(r, r_a) \, dv_a \, dv. \tag{3.62}$$

If the volume contains small separated regions which alone contribute to this energy, the elements $s_0 dv$ and $s._a dv_a$ may be replaced by quantities S_0 and $S._a$ respectively in the same way that in a region containing electric changes localized in small volumes the quantities, $\rho \, dv$, where ρ is the charge density may be replaced by a charge q.

The integrand is then replaced by a summation:

$$W = -\frac{\kappa^2}{4} \sum (S^*. S._a + S. S^*.) \phi(r, r_a)$$

or perhaps more conveniently by

$$W = -\frac{\kappa^2}{4} \sum_{a,b} (S^*._a S._b + S._a S^*._b) \phi(r_a, r_b), \tag{3.63}$$

the summation denoting a double summation over all the separate regions where the quantity $s.$ exists.

The vector field.

In the theory of the vector field the fundamental quantity is a five-vector (U_μ) corresponding to the electromagnetic potential vector (ϕ_m). In the case to be considered, it is convenient and sufficient for the present purpose to place $U_5 = 0$.

The field component corresponding to B_{mn} in the electromagnetic theory is denoted by $(F_{\mu\nu})$ derived according to the formula:

$$F_{\mu\nu} = \frac{\partial U_\nu}{\partial x^\mu} - \frac{\partial U_\mu}{\partial x^\nu}. \tag{3.64}$$

As a consequence of this

$$\frac{\partial F_{\mu\nu}}{\partial x^\lambda} + \frac{\partial F_{\nu\lambda}}{\partial x^\mu} + \frac{\partial F_{\lambda\mu}}{\partial x^\nu} = 0. \tag{3.65}$$

These equations correspond to (3.5) and (3.7) of the scalar field.

An antisymmetric tensor $(V^{\mu\nu})$ is also assumed to exist which satisfies the equation

$$\frac{\partial V^{\mu\nu}}{\partial x^\nu} = 0 \tag{3.66}$$

and a vector $(S_{\mu\nu})$ is defined by the relation:

$$F_{\mu\nu} = V_{\mu\nu} + S_{\mu\nu}. \tag{3.67}$$

The Lagrange function, which should be compared with that of the scalar field theory (3.42), is, in the case of the vector field,

$$L = \tfrac{1}{4}(F^{\mu\nu} F^*_{\mu\nu} - F^{\mu\nu} S^*_{\mu\nu} - F^{*\mu\nu} S_{\mu\nu}) \tag{3.68}$$

and the energy tensor is:

$$\begin{aligned}
\Theta^\mu_{\ \nu} &= \frac{\partial L}{\partial\left(\dfrac{\partial U_\alpha}{\partial x^\mu}\right)} \frac{\partial U_\alpha}{\partial x^\nu} + \frac{\partial L}{\partial\left(\dfrac{\partial U^*_\alpha}{\partial x^\mu}\right)} \frac{\partial U^*_\alpha}{\partial x^\nu} - \gamma^\mu_{\ \nu} L \\
&= \tfrac{1}{2}\left(V^{*\mu\alpha} \frac{\partial U_\alpha}{\partial x^\nu} + V^{\mu\alpha} \frac{\partial U^*_\alpha}{\partial x^\nu}\right) - \gamma^\mu_{\ \nu} L. \tag{3.69}
\end{aligned}$$

In this form $(\Theta^{\mu\nu})$ is not a symmetric tensor. It will appear later that it is important to derive the energy tensor in a symmetric form and the method of doing this will be explained.

The symmetrical tensor will be denoted by $(T^{\mu\nu})$ and it will be shown how it can be derived by the addition of a tensor $(Z^{\mu\nu})$ to $(\Theta^{\mu\nu})$, $Z^{\mu\nu}$ being derived by means of a relation

$$Z^{\mu\nu} = \frac{\partial H^{\lambda\mu\nu}}{\partial x^\lambda} \tag{3.70}$$

where $H^{\lambda\mu\nu} = -H^{\mu\lambda\nu}$. In this derivation the Lagrange equations are used so that the symmetry of $(T^{\mu\nu})$ results from the field equations and is not simply due to its form. As a result of this procedure it will be shown that the symmetric tensor is

$$T^\mu_{\ \nu} = \tfrac{1}{2}(V^{*\mu\alpha} F_{\nu\alpha} + V^{\mu\alpha} F^*_{\nu\alpha}) - \gamma^\mu_{\ \nu} L. \tag{3.71}$$

The energy from these field terms is given by

$$W = -\int T^4_{\ 4} \, dv$$

as in the previous case, and again it is to be noted that the theory is not complete until the form of the tensor $(S_{\mu\nu})$ is decided upon. It will appear later that it does not depend on the vector (U_μ). Moreover $(T^\mu_{\ \nu})$ is not conserved on account of the omission of the contribution made to it from $(S_{\mu\nu})$.

The Lagrange function can be expressed in the form

$$L = \tfrac{1}{8}(V^{*\mu\nu}F_{\mu\nu} - S^{*\mu\nu}F_{\mu\nu}) + \text{c.c.} \tag{3.72}$$

which is a convenient form for the calculation of the expression $\int L \, dv$ and of W.

If (l, k) can take only the values $1, 2, 3$, the first term in the bracket is

$$V^{*\mu\nu}F_{\mu\nu} = V^{*lk}F_{lk} + 2V^{*4k}F_{4k} + 2V^{*5m}F_{5m}, \quad (m = 1, 2, 3, 4)$$

$$\int V^{*lk}F_{lk} \, dv = \int V^{*lk}\left(\frac{\partial U_k}{\partial x^l} - \frac{\partial U_l}{\partial x^k}\right) dv = 2\int V^{*lk}\frac{\partial U_k}{\partial x^l} \, dv.$$

By partial integration, assuming that (U_k) vanishes at the boundary this becomes

$$-2\int U_k \frac{\partial V^{*lk}}{\partial x^l} \, dv.$$

By a similar process it may be shown that

$$\int V^{*4k}F_{4k} \, dv = \int V^{*4k}\frac{\partial U_k}{\partial x^4} \, dv + \int U_4 \frac{\partial V^{*4k}}{\partial x_k} \, dv.$$

Also

$$V^{*5m}F_{5m} = ikV^{*5m}U_m$$

and since

$$\frac{\partial V^{*5m}}{\partial x^5} = -ikV^{*5m}$$

on account of the factor e^{-ikx^5} in V^{*5m}, it follows that

$$\int V^{*\mu\nu}F_{\mu\nu} \, dv = \int 2\left\{\left(\frac{\partial V^{*ml}}{\partial x^l} + \frac{\partial V^{*m5}}{\partial x^5}\right)U_m + V^{*4l}\frac{\partial U_l}{\partial x^4}\right\} dv, \tag{3.73}$$

where summation over l is from 1 to 3 and over m from 1 to 4.

From the complex conjugate equation of (3.66),

$$\frac{\partial V^{*m\nu}}{\partial x^{\nu}} = \frac{\partial V^{*ml}}{\partial x^{l}} + \frac{\partial V^{*m4}}{\partial x^{4}} + \frac{\partial V^{*m5}}{\partial x^{5}} = 0.$$

Thus the expression (3.73) becomes

$$\int V^{*\mu\nu}F_{\mu\nu}\,dv = 2\int\left(V^{*4l}\frac{\partial U_{l}}{\partial x^{4}} + U_{l}\frac{\partial V^{*4l}}{\partial x^{4}}\right)dv$$

since $\qquad\qquad V^{*44} = 0$, this

$$= 2\int\frac{\partial}{\partial x^{4}}(V^{*4l}\,U_{l})\,dv. \qquad (3.74)$$

From (3.73) by replacing $V^{*\mu\nu}$ by $S^{*\mu\nu}$, it follows that

$$\int S^{*\mu\nu}F_{\mu\nu}\,dv = 2\int\left\{\left(\frac{\partial S^{*ml}}{\partial x^{l}} + \frac{\partial S^{*m5}}{\partial x^{5}}\right)U_{m} + S^{*4l}\frac{\partial U_{l}}{\partial x^{4}}\right\}dv. \qquad (3.75)$$

Thus $\qquad \int L\,dv = \tfrac{1}{4}\int\left\{\frac{\partial}{\partial x^{4}}(V^{*4l}\,U_{l}) - \left(\frac{\partial S^{*ml}}{\partial x^{l}} - ikS^{*m5}\right)U_{m}\right.$

$$\left. - S^{*4l}\frac{\partial U_{l}}{\partial x^{4}}\right\}dv + \text{c.c.} \qquad (3.76)$$

In order to determine the field energy the density $T^{4}{}_{4}$ is required and according to equation (3.71), the first term in the expression for the energy is

$$\tfrac{1}{2}\int V^{*4\alpha}F_{4\alpha}\,dv = \tfrac{1}{2}\int (V^{*4l}F_{4l} + V^{*45}F_{45})\,dv$$

$$= \tfrac{1}{2}\int\left(V^{*4l}\frac{\partial U_{l}}{\partial x^{4}} + U_{4}\frac{\partial V^{*4l}}{\partial x^{l}} - ikU_{4}\,V^{*45}\right)dv$$

after partial integration giving the second term in the bracket.

By the field equations

$$\frac{\partial V^{*4\nu}}{\partial x^{\nu}} = \frac{\partial V^{*4l}}{\partial x^{l}} - ikV^{*45} = 0.$$

Thus $\qquad\qquad \tfrac{1}{2}\int V^{*4\alpha}F_{4\alpha}\,dv = \tfrac{1}{2}\int V^{*4l}\frac{\partial U_{l}}{\partial x^{4}}\,dv.$

Thus $\qquad T^{4}{}_{4} = \tfrac{1}{4}\left\{V^{*4l}\frac{\partial U_{l}}{\partial x^{4}} - \frac{\partial V^{*4l}}{\partial x^{4}}U_{l} + \left(\frac{\partial S^{*ml}}{\partial x^{l}} - ikS^{*m5}\right)U_{m}\right.$

$$\left. + S^{*4l}\frac{\partial U_{l}}{\partial x^{4}}\right\} + \text{c.c.} \qquad (3.77)$$

and the energy

$$W = - \int T^4{}_4 \, dv. \qquad (3.78)$$

The nature and significance of these results is more easily appreciated if they are put into the form of the classical electromagnetic equations. This is readily done in the important case when the nuclear field is predominant, the gravitational and electromagnetic fields being negligible in comparison. Thus for all four-dimensional quantities there is no need to distinguish between contra- and co-variance.

The equation will be expressed in terms of vectors in accordance with substitutions like those of the table (3.2). The same letters will be used for the vectors but it must be kept in mind that the field is not electromagnetic. Thus the following substitutions will be made:

$$\left. \begin{aligned} V_{23} &= H_x, \quad V_{31} = H_y, \quad V_{12} = H_z, \\ V_{41} &= iD_x, \quad V_{42} = iD_y, \quad V_{43} = iD_z. \end{aligned} \right\} \qquad (3.79)$$

$$\left. \begin{aligned} F_{23} &= B_x, \quad F_{31} = B_y, \quad F_{12} = B_z, \\ F_{41} &= iE_x, \quad F_{42} = iE_y, \quad F_{43} = iE_z. \end{aligned} \right\} \qquad (3.80)$$

For the components of vector potential the substitutions:

$$U_1 = A_x, \quad U_2 = A_y, \quad U_3 = A_z, \quad U_4 = iV, \qquad (3.81)$$

will be made.

The magnetic and electric polarization densities will be introduced, respectively, by the relations:

$$\mathbf{B} = \mathbf{H} + \mathbf{I} \quad \text{and} \quad \mathbf{D} = \mathbf{E} + \mathbf{P} \qquad (3.82)$$

so that

$$\left. \begin{aligned} S_{23} &= I_x, \quad S_{31} = I_y, \quad S_{12} = I_z. \\ S_{41} &= -iP_x, \quad S_{42} = -iP_y, \quad S_{43} = -iP_z. \end{aligned} \right\} \qquad (3.83)$$

The field equations (3.64), (3.65) and (3.66) can now be put into the following form:

$$\left. \begin{aligned} \mathbf{B} &= \operatorname{curl} \mathbf{A}, \quad \mathbf{E} = -\frac{1}{c}\dot{\mathbf{A}} - \operatorname{grad} V, \\ \operatorname{div} \mathbf{B} &= 0, \quad \frac{1}{c}\dot{\mathbf{B}} = -\operatorname{curl} \mathbf{E}, \\ \operatorname{curl} \mathbf{H} &= \frac{1}{c}\dot{\mathbf{D}} - \kappa^2 \mathbf{A} + \mathbf{J}, \\ \operatorname{div} \mathbf{D} &= -\kappa^2 V + \rho. \end{aligned} \right\} \qquad (3.84)$$

The symbols J and ρ are used because these terms occupy the places of current and charge density, their values are:

$$J_k = -i\frac{k}{\gamma_{55}}S_{5k}, \quad \rho = -\frac{k}{\gamma_{55}}S_{54}.$$

The equation

$$\frac{\partial V^{5k}}{\partial x^k} + \frac{\partial V^{54}}{\partial x^4} = 0$$

becomes:

$$\kappa^2\left(\operatorname{div}\mathbf{A} + \frac{1}{c}\dot{V}\right) = \operatorname{div}\mathbf{J} + \frac{1}{c}\dot{\rho} \tag{3.85}$$

If the condition $[\operatorname{div}\mathbf{A} + (1/c)\dot{V}] = 0$ be adopted here corresponding to the relation in the electromagnetic theory, equation (3.85) implies also the conservation of the current vector (J_m) where $J_4 = i\rho$. Thus the right-hand side of equation (3.85) is equivalent to

$$\frac{k}{i\gamma_{55}}\frac{\partial S_5{}^m}{\partial x^m},$$

where m is summed over 1–4.

Thus the vanishing of the left-hand side of this equation implies the condition

$$\frac{\partial S_5{}^m}{\partial x^m} = 0. \tag{3.86}$$

In making use of the conjugate quantities containing the suffix 4, care must be taken in noting the significance of the term 'conjugate' in these cases (cf. 3.49). Thus in the case of $F_{4k} = iE_k$,

$$F_{4k} = -iF_{0k}, \quad F_{0k} = -E_k.$$

$$F_{4k}^* = -iF_{0k}^* = iE_k^*. \tag{3.87}$$

In the same way it can be shown that:

$$F^*{}_{54} = kV^*, \quad V^*{}_{4k} = iD_k^*, \quad S^*{}_{4k} = -iP_k^*, \quad S^*{}_{54} = \frac{\gamma_{55}}{k}\rho^*. \tag{3.88}$$

The equations (3.64), (3.65) and (3.66), except for the fact that a fifth coordinate is introduced, are identical in form with those proposed by Gustav Mie as the basis of the electromagnetic theory.

The application of these equations now to be made is to the static case. This means that the differential coefficient of any quantity with respect to the time will be placed equal to zero and by comparison with the equations of the electromagnetic theory the 'current', now represented by $\mathbf{J}$ is also placed equal to zero.

By means of equations (3.84) and (3.85) the vector $\mathbf{A}$ can be derived in terms of the polarization $\mathbf{I}$, as follows:

$$\operatorname{curl}^2 \mathbf{A} = \operatorname{curl} \mathbf{B} = \operatorname{curl} \mathbf{H} + \operatorname{curl} \mathbf{I},$$

$$\operatorname{curl} \mathbf{H} = -\kappa^2 \mathbf{A}.$$

Thus

$$\operatorname{curl}^2 \mathbf{A} = \operatorname{grad} \operatorname{div} \mathbf{A} - \nabla^2 \mathbf{A} = -\kappa^2 \mathbf{A} + \operatorname{curl} \mathbf{I}$$

and since from (3.85) $\operatorname{div} \mathbf{A} = 0$,

$$\nabla^2 \mathbf{A} - \kappa^2 \mathbf{A} = -\operatorname{curl} \mathbf{I}. \tag{3.89}$$

From comparison with equation (3.56) and the solution (3.61) it follows that

$$\mathbf{A} = \int (\operatorname{curl} I)_a \, \phi(r, r_a) \, dv_a \tag{3.90}$$

$$= \int (I_a \times \operatorname{grad}_a \phi) \, dv_a.$$

The equation for V can be obtained in the same way. Again from the equations (3.84) it follows that:

$$\nabla^2 V - \kappa^2 V = -\rho - \operatorname{div} \mathbf{P}. \tag{3.91}$$

In applications of this equation in the theory of the vector field, the polarization $\mathbf{P}$ is usually neglected but $\mathbf{I}$ is retained. This simplification is adopted here so that V will satisfy the equation

$$\nabla^2 V - \kappa^2 V = -\rho \tag{3.92}$$

and the solution is

$$V = \int \rho_a \, \phi(r, r_a) \, dv_a. \tag{3.93}$$

From equation (3.77) the energy density in the static case is

$$-T^4{}_4 = -\frac{1}{4} \left(\frac{\partial S^*{}_{ml}}{\partial x^l} - ik S^{*m5} \right) U_m + \text{c.c.} \tag{3.94}$$

and from the above substitutions

$$-T^4{}_4 = -\tfrac{1}{4} (\mathbf{A} . \operatorname{curl} \mathbf{I}^* + V \operatorname{div} \mathbf{P}^* + \mathbf{A} . \mathbf{J}^* - V\rho^*) + \text{c.c.} \tag{3.95}$$

67

Then imposing the relations for the static case and provided that all the quantities are real, $\mathbf{P}$ again being placed equal to zero, the right-hand side becomes

$$-\tfrac{1}{2}(\mathbf{A}.\operatorname{curl}\mathbf{I}- V\rho).$$

Thus

$$W = -\int T^4{}_4\,dv = -\tfrac{1}{2}\int (\mathbf{A}.\operatorname{curl}\mathbf{I}- V\rho)\,dv \qquad (3.96)$$

and after partial integration of the first term on the right-hand side, assuming that the quantity $\mathbf{I}$ vanishes at the boundary, it follows that

$$W = \tfrac{1}{2}\int (-\mathbf{I}.\mathbf{B}+ V\rho)\,dv. \qquad (3.97)$$

The second term on the right becomes, by means of the solution (3.93)

$$+\tfrac{1}{2}\iint \rho_a\rho_b\,\phi(r_a,r_b)\,dv_a\,dv_b \qquad (3.98)$$

but the first term requires some modification before it can be expressed in a convenient form.

It may be noted that a function of $\overline{\mathbf{r}_a-\mathbf{r}_b}$, such as ϕ, where

$$(\overline{\mathbf{r}_a-\mathbf{r}_b})^2 = (x_a-x_b)^2+(y_a-y_b)^2+(z_a-z_b)^2,$$

satisfies the condition

$$\operatorname{grad}_a\phi = -\operatorname{grad}_b\phi, \qquad (3.99)$$

where the suffix a denotes differentiation with respect to the co-ordinates (x_a,y_a,z_a) and b similarly with respect to (x_b,y_b,z_b).

Another relation that will be required is:

$$\operatorname{curl}(\mathbf{P}\times\mathbf{Q}) = \mathbf{P}\operatorname{div}\mathbf{Q}-\mathbf{Q}\operatorname{div}\mathbf{P}+(\mathbf{Q}.\operatorname{grad})\mathbf{P}-(\mathbf{P}.\operatorname{grad})\mathbf{Q}. \quad (3.100)$$

From equation (3.90) it appears that

$$\mathbf{B}_a = \operatorname{curl}_a\int \operatorname{curl}\mathbf{I}_b\,\phi(r_a,r_b)\,dv_b. \qquad (3.101)$$

The quantity $\mathbf{B}_a$ is the value at the point (x_a,y_a,z_a) and is a function of these coordinates. Similarly $\mathbf{I}_b$ is a function of (x_b,y_b,z_b) and does not contain (x_a,y_a,z_a), while ϕ is dependent on both sets. It thus follows from equation (3.100) that

$$\operatorname{curl}_a\int (\mathbf{I}_b\times\operatorname{grad}_b\phi)dv_b = \int \{\mathbf{I}_b\operatorname{div}_a(\operatorname{grad}_b\phi)-(\mathbf{I}_b.\operatorname{grad}_a)\operatorname{grad}_b\phi)\,dv_b$$

since $\operatorname{div}_a\mathbf{I}_b$ and $(\operatorname{grad}_b\phi.\operatorname{grad}_a)\mathbf{I}_b$ vanish.

Since $\operatorname{div}_a(\operatorname{grad}_b \phi) = -\operatorname{div}_b(\operatorname{grad}_b)\phi$, the integral can be written in the form:

$$-\int \{\mathbf{I}_b \nabla_b^2 \phi + (\mathbf{I}_b . \operatorname{grad}_b)\operatorname{grad}_a \phi\}\, dv_b. \qquad (3.102)$$

Thus according to equation (3.90) the value of $\mathbf{B}_a$ is given by (3.102) and the first term of the expression (3.97) for the energy, replacing $\nabla_b^2 \phi$ by $\kappa^2 \phi$, becomes

$$+\tfrac{1}{2}\int\int \{\kappa^2 \mathbf{I}_a . \mathbf{I}_b\, \phi(r_a, r_b) + (I_b . \operatorname{grad}_b)\,(I_a . \operatorname{grad}_a)\, \phi(r_a, r_b)\}\, dv_a\, dv_b \qquad (3.103)$$

and the total energy is given by the sum of the expressions (3.98) and (3.103).

In the case when the quantities represented by $\mathbf{I}$ and ρ are localized in small discrete volumes $\rho\, dv$ and $I\, dv$ will be represented by q and $\mathbf{m}$, and the energy may be written in the form:

$$W = \tfrac{1}{2}\sum_{a,b} \{q_a q_b + \kappa^2 \mathbf{m}_a . \mathbf{m}_b + (\mathbf{m}_b . \operatorname{grad}_b)(\mathbf{m}_a . \operatorname{grad}_a)\}\, \phi(r_a, r_b). \qquad (3.104)$$

In order to evaluate the third term of this expression, write

$$r_{ab}^2 = \sum_l (x_a^l - x_b^l)^2, \quad l = 1, 2, 3.$$

Then (3)

$$m_{al}\frac{\partial \phi}{\partial x_a^l} = (\mathbf{m}_a . \operatorname{grad}_a)\,\phi$$

and the term is

$$m_{bk}\, m_{al}\frac{\partial^2}{\partial x_b^k\, \partial x_a^l}\left(\frac{e^{-\kappa r_{ab}}}{r_{ab}}\right).$$

On carrying out the differentiation the expression is seen to be equal to

$$\left\{\mathbf{m}_a . \mathbf{m}_b\frac{1}{r_{ab}}\left(\kappa + \frac{1}{r_{ab}}\right) - \frac{(\mathbf{m}_a . \mathbf{r}_{ab})\,(\mathbf{m}_b . \mathbf{r}_{ab})}{r_{ab}^2}\left(\kappa^2 + \frac{3\kappa}{r_{ab}} + \frac{3}{r_{ab}^2}\right)\right\}\phi(r_a, r_b),$$

where $\mathbf{r}_{ab} = \mathbf{r}_a - \mathbf{r}_b$.

Thus the energy is:

$$W = \tfrac{1}{2}\sum_{a,b}\left\{q_a q_b + \tfrac{2}{3}\kappa^2 \mathbf{m}_a . \mathbf{m}_b\right.$$

$$\left. + \left(\frac{\kappa^2}{3} + \frac{\kappa}{r_{ab}} + \frac{1}{r_{ab}^2}\right)\left(\mathbf{m}_a . \mathbf{m}_b - \frac{3(\mathbf{m}_a . \mathbf{r}_{ab})(\mathbf{m}_b . \mathbf{r}_{ab})}{r_{ab}^2}\right)\right\}\phi(r_a, r_b). \qquad (3.105)$$

Dual vectors and tensors

Before proceeding to a study of two other types of field brought into prominence in the theory of the nuclear field it will be helpful to consider briefly the definition and some properties of dual vectors and tensors.

In the theory of determinants the coefficient $e_{\alpha\beta\gamma\ldots}$ occurs, where the number of suffixes is equal to the number of rows or columns of the determinant. The coefficient can be described as completely antisymmetric, which means that the interchange of neighbouring suffixes changes its sign. To illustrate this point in the case of three suffixes $e_{123} = -e_{213} = e_{231}$.

It is noticed that the sign changes from that of e_{123} for an odd number of changes of suffixes but remains unchanged for an even number of changes. This applies in the general case.

The values which the coefficient can assume are 1, -1 and 0 and the rule adopted is that $e_{123\ldots} = +1$. The value of $e_{\alpha\beta\gamma\ldots}$ is -1 if an odd number of displacements is required to restore the sequence $123\ldots$ and $+1$ if the number is even. If any two suffixes are equal the value is zero.

Coefficients $e^{\alpha\beta\gamma\cdots}$ are also introduced with the same properties. They introduce a symmetry into the notation and are essential when the components of the determinants are also tensor components.

For simplicity a determinant of two rows and two columns can serve as an illustration of the use of these coefficients.

Let

$$a = |a_{\alpha\beta}| = \begin{vmatrix} a_{11} & a_{12} \\ a_{21} & a_{22} \end{vmatrix}.$$

The value, a, of the determinant is defined by

$$a e_{\alpha\beta} = e^{\lambda\mu} a_{\alpha\lambda} a_{\beta\mu}. \tag{3.106}$$

This is easily verified, remembering that summation occurs over λ and μ for the values 1, 2.

Another way of writing (3.106) is

$$a = e^{12} e^{\lambda\mu} a_{1\lambda} a_{2\mu}. \tag{3.107}$$

The notation can be extended and the case of the determinant

$$\gamma = |\gamma_{\mu\nu}|$$

is of particular interest, the components being the coefficients of the five-dimensional line element. In this case

$$\left.\begin{array}{l} \gamma e_{\alpha\beta\gamma\delta\epsilon} = e^{\lambda\mu\nu\rho\sigma} \gamma_{\alpha\lambda} \gamma_{\beta\mu} \gamma_{\gamma\nu} \gamma_{\delta\rho} \gamma_{\epsilon\sigma}, \\ \gamma = e^{12345} e^{\lambda\mu\nu\rho\sigma} \gamma_{1\lambda} \gamma_{2\mu} \gamma_{3\nu} \gamma_{4\rho} \gamma_{5\sigma}. \end{array}\right\} \quad (3.108)$$

The result required can, however, be illustrated by means of a two-rowed determinant for the sake of brevity, the more general result following by analogy.

Let it be supposed that a_{mn} is a component of a two-dimensional covariant tensor and let the determinant

$$a = |a_{mn}|.$$

Thus

$$a e_{kl} = e^{mn} a_{km} a_{ln} \quad (3.109)$$

and from this it follows that

$$2! \, a = e^{kl} e^{mn} a_{km} a_{ln} \quad (3.110)$$

since the double suffixes on the right imply summation of k and l over 1 and 2, giving 2! times the expression (3.107).

Suppose that a general transformation of coordinates now takes place. The value of a becomes a' where

$$2! \, a' = e^{kl} \frac{\partial x^\alpha}{\partial x'^k} \frac{\partial x^\rho}{\partial x'^l} e^{mn} \frac{\partial x^\beta}{\partial x'^m} \frac{\partial x^\sigma}{\partial x'^n} a_{\alpha\beta} a_{\rho\sigma}$$

the terms being arranged for convenience.

If Δ denotes the determinant

$$\left| \frac{\partial x^r}{\partial x'^s} \right|$$

by comparison with (3.109),

$$\Delta e^{\alpha\rho} = e^{kl} \frac{\partial x^\alpha}{\partial x'^k} \frac{\partial x^\rho}{\partial x'^l},$$

$e^{\alpha\rho}$ being written with the suffixes raised to correspond with the positions of α and ρ on the right-hand side of the equation. Thus

$$2! \, a' = \Delta^2 e^{\alpha\rho} e^{\beta\sigma} a_{\alpha\beta} a_{\rho\sigma} = 2! \, \Delta^2 a$$

from which it follows that

$$\Delta = \left(\frac{a'}{a}\right)^{1/2}. \quad (3.111)$$

In the same way it can be shown that

$$\left|\frac{\partial x'^m}{\partial x^n}\right| = \left(\frac{a}{a'}\right)^{1/2}. \tag{3.112}$$

Thus from the relation corresponding to that of (3.109)

$$\varDelta e_{\alpha\beta} = e_{\lambda\mu}\frac{\partial x^\lambda}{\partial x'^\alpha}\frac{\partial x^\mu}{\partial x'^\beta}$$

it follows that

$$(a')^{1/2}e_{\alpha\beta} = \frac{\partial x^\lambda}{\partial x'^\alpha}\frac{\partial x^\mu}{\partial x'^\beta}a^{1/2}e_{\lambda\mu} \tag{3.113}$$

and it is evident that $a^{1/2}e_{\lambda\mu}$ transforms like a covariant tensor.

The example of this property required for the present purpose is that of the determinant γ, in which case the extension of the relation (3.113) shows that $(\gamma^{1/2}e_{\alpha\beta\gamma\delta\epsilon})$ is a covariant tensor of the fifth rank. From the relation (3.112) it follows similarly that $(e^{\alpha\beta\gamma\delta\epsilon}/\gamma^{1/2})$ is a contravariant tensor.

These are denoted respectively by $\epsilon_{\alpha\beta\gamma\delta\epsilon}$ and $\epsilon^{\alpha\beta\gamma\delta\epsilon}$ and in application of these results it will be assumed that $\gamma = 1$.

The tensors concerned in this discussion are completely antisymmetric and certain pairs are related by means of the coefficients $\epsilon_{\alpha\beta\gamma\delta\epsilon}$ and $\epsilon^{\alpha\beta\gamma\delta\epsilon}$.

Thus a tensor $(A^{\alpha\beta\gamma})$ is related to a tensor $(B_{\delta\epsilon})$ by means of

$$A^{\alpha\beta\gamma} = \frac{1}{2!}\epsilon^{\alpha\beta\gamma\delta\epsilon}B_{\delta\epsilon}. \tag{3.114}$$

The factor $1/2!$ is introduced to reduce the number of terms occurring on the right-hand side as a result of interchange of the suffixes δ and ϵ. The multiplicity of terms arises through the fact that $B_{\delta\epsilon} = -B_{\epsilon\delta}$ and at the same time the sign of the coefficient is changed.

$(A^{\alpha\beta\gamma})$ and $(B_{\delta\epsilon})$ are described as dual tensors. Another pair of this kind is $(A^{\alpha\beta})$ and $B_{\gamma\delta\epsilon}$ where

$$A^{\alpha\beta} = \frac{1}{3!}\epsilon^{\alpha\beta\gamma\delta\epsilon}B_{\gamma\delta\epsilon} \tag{3.115}$$

and a tensor and vector are related by

$$A^{\alpha\beta\gamma\delta} = \epsilon^{\alpha\beta\gamma\delta\epsilon}B_\epsilon. \tag{3.116}$$

It is convenient to introduce the symbol $\delta^{\alpha\beta\gamma\cdots}_{\lambda\mu\nu\cdots}$ in which α, β, γ, etc., may have any values 1 to n and similarly for λ, μ, ν, etc.

Thus in $\delta^{\alpha\beta\gamma}_{\lambda\mu\nu}$ each of the three suffixes may have the values 1 to 5. If α, β and γ denote the same numbers as λ, μ, ν but differently arranged the value of the symbol is $+1$ or -1 according as λ, μ, ν can be brought into the same order as α, β, γ by an even or odd number of interchanges. In other cases the value is zero.

Consider

$$\epsilon^{\alpha_1 \alpha_2 \ldots \alpha_r \alpha_{r+1} \ldots \alpha_n} \epsilon_{\beta_1 \beta_2 \ldots \beta_r \alpha_{r+1} \ldots \alpha_n}.$$

This means that there are n symbols in each of the rows of suffixes capable of assuming the values 1 to n of which the last $(n-r)$ are alike in the two rows and summation is therefore implied. There are thus $(n-r)!$ ways of arranging these suffixes, and the sign of the expression will depend on the arrangement of the numbers $(\beta_1 \ldots \beta_r)$ with respect to the numbers $(\alpha_1 \ldots \alpha_r)$. The expression is thus

$$e^{\alpha_1 \alpha_2 \ldots \alpha_r \alpha_{r+1} \ldots \alpha_n} \epsilon_{\beta_1 \beta_2 \ldots \beta_r \alpha_{r+1} \ldots \alpha_r} = (n-r)!\, \delta^{\alpha_1 \alpha_2 \ldots \alpha_r}_{\beta_1 \beta_2 \ldots \beta_r}. \quad (3.117)$$

It is of course of no consequence in what sequence the numbers $(\alpha_1 \ldots \alpha_r)$ are placed with respect to $(\alpha_{r+1}$ to $\alpha_n)$, the point being that $(n-r)$ of these occur in a group in front of or behind the remainder, provided that in the lower row they occupy the corresponding position with respect to the suffixes $(\beta_1 \ldots \beta_r)$.

From the expression (3.114),

$$\epsilon_{\alpha\beta\gamma\lambda\mu} A^{\alpha\beta\gamma} = \frac{1}{2!} \epsilon_{\alpha\beta\gamma\lambda\mu} \epsilon^{\alpha\beta\gamma\delta\epsilon} B_{\delta\epsilon} = \frac{3!}{2!} \delta^{\delta\epsilon}_{\lambda\mu} B_{\delta\epsilon},$$

δ and ϵ must have the same values as λ and μ but in the summation these values can be interchanged. Thus the result is

$$B_{\lambda\mu} = \frac{1}{3!} \epsilon_{\alpha\beta\gamma\lambda\mu} A^{\alpha\beta\gamma}. \quad (3.118)$$

The relations

$$\left.\begin{array}{l} B_{\lambda\mu\nu} = \dfrac{1}{2!} \epsilon_{\alpha\beta\lambda\mu\nu} A^{\alpha\beta} \\[2ex] B_\epsilon = \dfrac{1}{4!} \epsilon_{\alpha\beta\gamma\delta\epsilon} A^{\alpha\beta\gamma\delta} \end{array}\right\} \quad (3.119)$$

and

can be obtained in the same way.

The pseudo-vector field

The equations (3.7) and (3.8) for the scalar field and (3.64) and (3.65) suggest the consideration of equations in the case of fields in which the components are tensors of higher rank. The tensors of next higher rank are $(F_{\lambda\mu\nu})$ and $(V^{\lambda\mu\nu})$ and the equations:

$$\frac{\partial F_{\mu\nu\rho}}{\partial x^{\lambda}} - \frac{\partial F_{\nu\rho\lambda}}{\partial x^{\mu}} + \frac{\partial F_{\rho\lambda\mu}}{\partial x^{\nu}} - \frac{\partial F_{\lambda\mu\nu}}{\partial x^{\rho}} = 0 \tag{3.120}$$

and

$$\frac{\partial V^{\lambda\mu\nu}}{\partial x^{\nu}} = 0. \tag{3.121}$$

The latter equation represents the vanishing of the divergence of the tensor $(V^{\lambda\mu\nu})$.

In general the form of the divergence of $(V^{\lambda\mu\nu})$ is more complicated than this equation suggests (cf. 2.101) but on account of the complete antisymmetry of the tensor and the fact that γ has the value unity, the expression for the divergence reduces to the left-hand side of equation (3.121).

The dual tensors of $(F_{\lambda\mu\nu})$ and $(V^{\lambda\mu\nu})$ are introduced and equations for terms of the second rank result. The use of the letters F and V will be continued but it must be remembered that they are different quantities from those in the section on the vector field. The tensors of the second rank in the pseudo-vector field, $(F_{\mu\nu})$, $(V_{\mu\nu})$ are not the same as those represented by the same symbols in the vector field. Thus

$$F_{\lambda\mu\nu} = \frac{1}{2!} \epsilon_{\lambda\mu\nu\alpha\beta} F^{\alpha\beta} \tag{3.122}$$

and

$$V^{\lambda\mu\nu} = \frac{1}{2!} \epsilon^{\lambda\mu\nu\alpha\beta} V_{\alpha\beta}. \tag{3.123}$$

Taking care of the signs of the coefficients $(\epsilon_{\lambda\mu\nu\rho\sigma})$ it appears that equation (3.120) becomes

$$\frac{\partial F^{\mu\nu}}{\partial x^{\nu}} = 0 \tag{3.124}$$

and (3.121) becomes

$$\frac{\partial V_{\mu\nu}}{\partial x^{\lambda}} + \frac{\partial V_{\nu\lambda}}{\partial x^{\mu}} + \frac{\partial V_{\lambda\mu}}{\partial x^{\nu}} = 0 \tag{3.125}$$

for values of λ, μ, ν from 1 to 5.

The second of these field equations can thus be satisfied by the assumption

$$V_{\alpha\beta} = \frac{\partial U_{\beta}}{\partial x^{\alpha}} - \frac{\partial U_{\alpha}}{\partial x^{\beta}}. \tag{3.126}$$

The tensor $(S^{\lambda\mu\nu})$ is defined by the relations

$$F^{\lambda\mu\nu} = V^{\lambda\mu\nu} + S^{\lambda\mu\nu} \tag{3.127}$$

and the dual tensor by

$$F_{\lambda\mu} = V_{\lambda\mu} + S_{\lambda\mu}. \tag{3.128}$$

In the Lagrange density function $V^{\mu\nu}$ and $F_{\mu\nu}$ change places in that of the vector field (3.68). Hence now

$$L = \tfrac{1}{4}(V^{\mu\nu} V^*{}_{\mu\nu} + V^{\mu\nu} S^*{}_{\mu\nu} + V^{*\mu\nu} S_{\mu\nu}). \tag{3.129}$$

The change in sign in the second and third terms is accounted for by the fact that $(S_{\lambda\mu})$ stays on the same side when $F_{\lambda\mu}$ and $V_{\lambda\mu}$ are interchanged (cf. 3.67). The field equation (3.124) follows in the usual way as also does the energy tensor

$$T^{\mu}{}_{\nu} = \tfrac{1}{2}(F^{*\mu\alpha} V_{\nu\alpha} + F^{\mu\alpha} V^*{}_{\nu\alpha}) - \gamma^{\mu}{}_{\nu} L. \tag{3.130}$$

By comparison with equation (3.72) it appears that

$$L = \tfrac{1}{8}(F^{*\mu\nu} V_{\mu\nu} + S^{*\mu\nu} V_{\mu\nu}) + \text{c.c.} \tag{3.131}$$

Again in order that the results obtained may be expressed in a familiar notation the following substitutions are made similar to those made in the case of the vector field (3.79 sqq.).

$$\left.\begin{array}{llll}
F_{23} = B_x, \text{ etc.}, & F_{4k} = iE_k, & F^*_{4k} = iE^*_k, \\
V_{23} = H_x, \text{ etc.}, & V_{4k} = iD_k, & V^*_{4k} = iD^*_k, \\
U_k = A_k, & U_4 = iV, & U^*_4 = iV^* \\
S_{23} = I_x, \text{ etc.}, & S_{4k} = -iP_k, & S^*_{4k} = -iP^*_k,
\end{array}\right\} \tag{3.132}$$

If also

$$S_{5k} = -\frac{i\gamma_{55}}{k}J_k, \quad S_{54} = \frac{\gamma_{55}}{k}\rho, \quad S^*_{54} = -\frac{\gamma_{55}}{k}\rho^*, \tag{3.133}$$

the field equations (3.124) become

$$\left.\begin{array}{r}
\operatorname{curl}\mathbf{B} - \dfrac{\dot{\mathbf{E}}}{c} = \mathbf{J} - \kappa^2 \mathbf{A} \\[2mm]
\operatorname{div}\mathbf{E} = \rho - \kappa^2 V \\[2mm]
\kappa^2\left(\operatorname{div}\mathbf{A} + \dfrac{V}{c}\right) = \operatorname{div}\mathbf{J} + \dfrac{\dot{\rho}}{c}
\end{array}\right\} \tag{3.134}$$

and the equations (3.125) become

$$\left.\begin{array}{ll}
\operatorname{curl}\mathbf{D} = -\dfrac{\dot{\mathbf{H}}}{c}, & \mathbf{D} = -\operatorname{grad}V - \dfrac{1}{c}\dot{\mathbf{A}} \\[2mm]
\operatorname{div}\mathbf{H} = 0, & \mathbf{H} = \operatorname{curl}\mathbf{A}
\end{array}\right\} \tag{3.135}$$

and the relation (3.128) gives

$$\mathbf{B} = \mathbf{H} + \mathbf{I} \qquad \mathbf{E} = \mathbf{D} - \mathbf{P}. \tag{3.136}$$

By the same process as that used to arrive at equation (3.74) in the case of the vector field it can be shown that from equation (3.131) it follows that

$$\int L \, dv = \frac{1}{4} \int \frac{\partial}{\partial x^4} (F^{*4l} U_l) \, dv - \frac{1}{4} \int U_m \left(\frac{\partial S^{*lm}}{\partial x^l} - ikS^{*5m} \right) dv$$
$$+ \frac{1}{4} \int S^{*4l} \frac{\partial U_l}{\partial x^4} dv + \text{c.c.} \tag{3.137}$$

$(l = 1, 2, 3; \, m = 1, 2, 3, 4)$.

From equation (3.130) it follows similarly that

$$W = -\int T^4{}_4 \, dv = \frac{1}{4} \int \left(\frac{\partial F^{*4l}}{\partial x^4} U_l - F^{*4l} \frac{\partial U_l}{\partial x^4} \right) dv$$
$$- \frac{1}{4} \int U_m \left(\frac{\partial S^{*lm}}{\partial x^l} - ikS^{*5m} \right) dv$$
$$+ \frac{1}{4} \int S^{*4l} \frac{\partial U_l}{\partial x^4} dv + \text{c.c.} \tag{3.138}$$

In the static case the differential coefficients with respect to x^4 vanish and the energy density is then

$$W_0 = \tfrac{1}{4} U_m \left(\frac{\partial S^{*ml}}{\partial x^l} - ikS^{*m5} \right) + \text{c.c.}, \tag{3.139}$$

S^{*ml} and S^{*m5} replacing $-S^{*lm}$ and $-S^{*5m}$ respectively.

This appears in a more familiar form by means of the substitutions (3.132) and (3.133), becoming:

$$W_0 = \tfrac{1}{4}(\mathbf{A} . \operatorname{curl} \mathbf{I}^* + V \operatorname{div} \mathbf{P}^* - \mathbf{A} . \mathbf{J}^* + V\rho^*) + \text{c.c.} \tag{3.140}$$

and, if the quantities occurring here are all real,

$$W_0 = \tfrac{1}{2}(\mathbf{A} . \operatorname{curl} \mathbf{I} + V \operatorname{div} \mathbf{P} - \mathbf{A} . \mathbf{J} + V\rho). \tag{3.141}$$

This quantity is integrated to give the total energy so that since

$$\int (\mathbf{A} . \operatorname{curl} \mathbf{I} + V \operatorname{div} \mathbf{P}) \, dv = \int (\mathbf{I} . \operatorname{curl} \mathbf{A} - \mathbf{P} \operatorname{grad} V) \, dv,$$

it follows that the density may be written in the form:

$$W_0 = \tfrac{1}{2}(\mathbf{I} . \operatorname{curl} \mathbf{A} - \mathbf{P} . \operatorname{grad} V - \mathbf{A} . \mathbf{J} + V\rho), \tag{3.142}$$

the values of $\mathbf{I}$ and $\mathbf{P}$ being assumed to vanish at the boundary.

From the field equations (3.134) and (3.135), assuming that $\dot{\mathbf{E}}$, $\dot{V}$ and $\dot{\rho}$ are zero, it follows that

$$\nabla^2 V - \kappa^2 V = -\rho - \operatorname{div} \mathbf{P}$$

and

$$\nabla^2 \mathbf{A} - \kappa^2 \mathbf{A} = \frac{1}{\kappa^2} \operatorname{grad} \operatorname{div} \mathbf{J} - \mathbf{J} + \operatorname{curl} \mathbf{I}. \tag{3.143}$$

The solutions of these equations have already been considered (cf. 3.59).

If all the quantities, ρ, $\mathbf{J}$, $\mathbf{I}$ and $\mathbf{P}$ exist, the evaluation of the energy is complicated. A case which has been considered in the nuclear theory, is that in which $\mathbf{I}$ and ρ are placed equal to zero when

$$W_0 = \tfrac{1}{2}(\mathbf{P}.\mathbf{D} - \mathbf{A}.\mathbf{J}) \tag{3.144}$$

grad V being substituted by $\mathbf{D}$ from the equations (3.135) for the case when $\dot{\mathbf{A}} = 0$.

In this case the value of V at a point (x_a, y_a, z_a) is

$$V_a = \int \operatorname{div}_b \mathbf{P} \phi(r_a, r_b)\, dv_b \tag{3.145}$$

and the value of $\mathbf{A}$ is

$$\mathbf{A}_a = \int \left\{ \mathbf{J}_b - \frac{1}{\kappa^2} (\operatorname{grad} \operatorname{div} \mathbf{J})_b \right\} \phi(r_a, r_b)\, dv_b. \tag{3.146}$$

Remembering that in the case now considered

$$\mathbf{D} = -\operatorname{grad} V,$$

the first term of (3.144) makes the contribution

$$-\tfrac{1}{2} \iint \mathbf{P}_a \operatorname{grad}_a \{ \operatorname{div}_b \mathbf{P} \phi(r_a, r_b) \}\, dv_a\, dv_b, \tag{3.147}$$

and the second term makes the contribution

$$-\tfrac{1}{2} \iint \mathbf{J}_a . \left\{ \mathbf{J}_b - \frac{1}{\kappa^2} (\operatorname{grad} \operatorname{div} \mathbf{J})_b \right\} \phi(r_a, r_b)\, dv_a\, dv_b \text{ to } W. \tag{3.148}$$

By partial integration with respect to the coordinates (x_b, y_b, z_b), assuming again that the quantities concerned vanish at the boundary, the first term can be transformed to

$$\tfrac{1}{2} \iint \mathbf{P}_a . \operatorname{grad}_a (\mathbf{P}_b . \operatorname{grad}_b) \phi(r_a, r_b)\, dv_a\, dv_b. \tag{3.149}$$

The second term of the expression (3.148) gives by partial integration

$$-\frac{1}{2\kappa^2} \int \int \operatorname{div}_b \mathbf{J}\mathbf{J}_a \cdot \operatorname{grad}_b \phi \, dv_a dv_b$$

and remembering the relation (3.99) this becomes

$$\frac{1}{2\kappa^2} \int \int (\mathbf{J}_a \cdot \operatorname{grad}_a) \phi \operatorname{div}_b \mathbf{J} \, dv_a dv_b$$

and after another partial integration the expression becomes

$$-\frac{1}{2\kappa^2} \int \int (\mathbf{J}_b \cdot \operatorname{grad}_b)(\mathbf{J}_a \cdot \operatorname{grad}_a) \phi(r_a, r_b) \, dv_a dv_b.$$

Thus the total energy is

$$W = \tfrac{1}{2} \int \int \left\{ (\mathbf{P}_a \cdot \operatorname{grad}_a)(\mathbf{P}_b \cdot \operatorname{grad}_b) - \mathbf{J}_a \cdot \mathbf{J}_b \right.$$

$$\left. - \frac{1}{\kappa^2}(\mathbf{J}_a \cdot \operatorname{grad}_a)(\mathbf{J}_b \cdot \operatorname{grad}_b) \right\} \phi \, dv_a dv_b \qquad (3.150)$$

changing the order in the last term for the sake of symmetry and this is possible since J_a is independent of (x_b, y_b, z_b) and J_b of (x_a, y_a, z_a).

As in the previous cases the expression for the energy can be put into the form of a double summation applicable when small isolated regions are the seats of polarization or current.

The pseudo-scalar field

The case of the pseudo-vector field in which the field tensors are the antisymmetric tensors $(F_{\lambda\mu\nu})$ and $(V^{\lambda\mu\nu})$ suggests the consideration of a field in which the tensors are of the fourth rank $(F_{\lambda\mu\nu\rho})$ and $(V^{\lambda\mu\nu\rho})$. The field equations corresponding to those of (3.120) and (3.121) are:

$$\frac{\partial F_{\mu\nu\rho\sigma}}{\partial x^\lambda} + \frac{\partial F_{\nu\rho\sigma\lambda}}{\partial x^\mu} + \frac{\partial F_{\rho\sigma\lambda\mu}}{\partial x^\nu} + \frac{\partial F_{\sigma\lambda\mu\nu}}{\partial x^\rho} + \frac{\partial F_{\lambda\mu\nu\rho}}{\partial x^\sigma} = 0 \qquad (3.151)$$

and

$$\frac{\partial V^{\lambda\mu\nu\rho}}{\partial x^\rho} = 0, \qquad (3.152)$$

the latter expressing the vanishing of the divergence of a completely antisymmetric tensor, with $\gamma = 1$.

If the dual quantities, in this case dual vectors, are introduced by means of the relations

$$\left.\begin{aligned}
F_{\lambda\mu\nu\sigma} &= \epsilon_{\lambda\mu\nu\sigma\epsilon} F^\epsilon \\
V^{\lambda\mu\nu\rho} &= \epsilon^{\lambda\mu\nu\rho\epsilon} V_\epsilon,
\end{aligned}\right\} \tag{3.153}$$

and

equation (3.151) becomes

$$\frac{\partial F^\epsilon}{\partial x^\epsilon} = 0, \tag{3.154}$$

since $\lambda, \mu, \nu, \rho, \sigma$ are all different numbers from 1 to 5 so that ϵ in the five terms has the values 1 to 5.

The equation (3.152) becomes

$$\frac{\partial}{\partial x^\rho}(\epsilon^{\lambda\mu\nu\rho\epsilon} V_\epsilon) = 0.$$

Thus ρ and ϵ are summed over the two values out of the five not possessed by λ, μ, ν and the equation is thus

$$\frac{\partial V_\epsilon}{\partial x^\rho} - \frac{\partial V_\rho}{\partial x^\epsilon} = 0 \tag{3.155}$$

and ϵ and ρ can have any pair of the five values.

As in the previous cases a quantity $(S_{\lambda\mu\nu\rho})$, this time a tensor of the fourth rank, is defined by

$$\left.\begin{aligned}
F_{\lambda\mu\nu\rho} &= V_{\lambda\mu\nu\rho} + S_{\lambda\mu\nu\rho} \\
F'^\epsilon &= V^\epsilon + S^\epsilon.
\end{aligned}\right\} \tag{3.156}$$

or, in terms of the dual vectors

From the equation (3.155), it follows that

$$V_\epsilon = \frac{\partial\theta}{\partial x^\epsilon}, \quad \text{(cf. 3.5)}, \tag{3.157}$$

where $\theta = V_5/ik$.

The field equations can be expressed in the form of those of the scalar field, (3.13) sqq., and they can be obtained from them by interchanging the letters V and F, and by writing $-S$ instead of S. This follows as in the case of the pseudo-vector field from the consideration that (V_ϵ) is now the gradient of a vector and if V_ϵ is replaced by F'_ϵ, F^ϵ by V'^ϵ_i, and S_ϵ by $-S_\epsilon'$, then

$$F^\epsilon = V^\epsilon + S^\epsilon$$

becomes

$$F'^\epsilon = V'^\epsilon + S'^\epsilon.$$

This is the contravariant form of equation (3.6) and the field equations (3.154) and (3.155) become (3.9) and (3.7) except that the symbols are V'^μ and F'^μ respectively.

The Lagrange function of the pseudo-scalar field

With these considerations and by reference to the expression (3.42) it is evident that in the present case the Lagrange function

$$L = \tfrac{1}{2}(V^{*\mu}\,V_\mu + S^{*\mu}\,V_\mu + S^\mu\,V^*_\mu) \tag{3.158}$$

and the energy tensor is

$$\Theta^\mu_{\ \nu} = \tfrac{1}{2}(F^{*\mu}\,V_\nu + F^\mu\,V^*_\nu) - \gamma^\mu_{\ \nu}\,L. \tag{3.159}$$

By comparison with equation (3.50) it appears that

$$L = \tfrac{1}{4}(F^{*\mu}\,V_\mu + S^{*\mu}\,V_\mu) + \text{c.c.} \tag{3.160}$$

and consequently by comparison with (3.52)

$$\int L\,dv = \tfrac{1}{4}\int\left\{\frac{1}{ik}\left(V_5\frac{\partial F^{*4}}{\partial x^4} + F^{*4}\frac{\partial V_5}{\partial x^4}\right) + S^{*\mu}\,V_\mu\right\}dv + \text{c.c.} \tag{3.161}$$

and from (3.53)

$$\int H\,dv = \frac{1}{4ik}\int\left(F^{*4}\frac{\partial V_5}{\partial x^4} - V_5\frac{\partial F^{*4}}{\partial x^4}\right)dv - \tfrac{1}{4}\int S^{*\mu}\,V_\mu\,dv + \text{c.c.} \tag{3.162}$$

The field equation (3.154) after substitution by means of the relation (3.156) gives:

$$\frac{\partial V^\mu}{\partial x^\mu} = -\frac{\partial S^\mu}{\partial x^\mu}$$

and in the static case it follows that

$$\nabla^2 v_{\,.} - \kappa^2 v_{\,.} = -i\kappa\,\text{div}\,\mathbf{s} + \kappa^2 s_{\,.}, \tag{3.163}$$

where the use of small letters is in accordance with the notation introduced in the equations (2.60) sqq. and $\mathbf{s}$ denotes a vector with components (S_k), k having the values $(1,2,3)$.

The solution of this equation (cf. 3.60) is

$$v_{\,.a} = \int\{i\kappa(\text{div}\,\mathbf{s})_b - \kappa^2 s_{\,.b}\}\,\phi\,dv_b, \tag{3.164}$$

the suffixes a and b denoting as before that the quantities are calculated at points (x_a, y_a, z_a) and (x_b, y_b, z_b) respectively.

In an application of this result in the theory of the nuclear field s. has been placed equal to zero. In the static case, with this assumption the total energy of the field given by equation (3.162) is

$$W = -\tfrac{1}{4} \int (s_a^{*k} v_{ak} + s_a^k v_{ak}^*) \, dv_a + \text{c.c.} \qquad (3.165)$$

$v_4 = \partial\theta/\partial x^4$ being zero in the static case. But

$$v_k = \frac{1}{i\kappa} \frac{\partial v}{\partial x^k},$$

so that after partial integration under the conditions assumed in the previous cases

$$W = \tfrac{1}{4} \int (s^{*k} \operatorname{grad}_k)_a (s^l \operatorname{grad}_l) \, \phi(r_a, r_b) \, dv_a \, dv_b + \text{c.c.} \qquad (3.166)$$

Bibliography

1. G. MIE, 1912. *Annln Phys.* **37**, 511, 391.
2. F. HUND, 1954. *Materie als Feld.* Springer.
3. L. DE BROGLIE, 1945. *De la Mécanique Ondulatoire à la Théorie du Noyau.* Hermann et Cie.
4. W. PAULI, 1941. *Rev. mod. Phys.* **13** (3), 203.
5. N. KEMMER, 1938. *Proc. R. Soc.* A, **167**, 125.
6. E. M. WILLIAMSON, 1953. *Nuovo Cim.* **X**, 2, 113.

CHAPTER 4

The Symmetric Energy Tensor and the Tensor of Moment of Momentum

It has already been stated that the energy tensor $(\Theta^{\mu\nu})$ is not in general symmetric $(\Theta^{\mu\nu} \neq \Theta^{\nu\mu})$. The fact that it is conserved has made it an important quantity in all field theories, where it occurs as the representative of energy, momentum and current density.

But in the structure of the tensor of moment of momentum the energy tensor is required in a symmetric form. It becomes necessary to examine the possibility of constructing a symmetric tensor $(T^{\mu\nu})$ which has the important properties of $(\Theta^{\mu\nu})$ in that it is conserved and gives the same values of total energy, momentum and electrical charge.

In order to obtain this tensor the method adopted is that of examining the effect of an infinitesimal transformation of coordinates of the kind:

$$x'^{\mu} = x^{\mu} + \xi^{\mu}, \tag{4.1}$$

where (ξ^{μ}) represents a set of small arbitrary quantities of the first order of magnitude (1), (2).

For the present purpose these will take the form:

$$\xi^{\mu} = a^{\mu}_{\ \nu} x^{\nu}, \tag{4.2}$$

the coefficients $(a^{\mu}_{\ \nu})$ being constant quantities of the first order. The transformations considered are thus of the Lorentz type.

From the examination of this special case results of general application may be obtained since the invariance of tensor relations does not depend on the type of transformation.

It will be assumed that the coefficients $(a^{\mu}_{\ \nu})$ are antisymmetric $(a^{\mu}_{\ \nu} = -a_{\nu}^{\ \mu})$, and that they are arbitrary. The type of transformation can be described as an infinitesimal rotation by comparison with a small rotation of the axes of x and y about the axis z, when the relations are:

$$x' = x + \theta y, \quad y' = y - \theta x$$

θ denoting a small angle.

Under these circumstances

$$x'^\mu x'_\mu = x^\mu x_\mu,$$

neglecting quantities of the second and higher orders. The invariant quantity to be considered under this transformation is the Lagrange function L.

From the assumption of invariance, $(\delta L = 0)$, it will be found that a relation of the type:

$$\delta L = a^\mu_{\ \nu} t_\mu^{\ \nu} = 0 \tag{4.3}$$

is obtained, and since $a^\mu_{\ \nu}$ is antisymmetric, $t_\mu^{\ \nu}$ must be symmetric.

The comparison of this tensor with $(\Theta_\mu^{\ \nu})$ then leads to the adoption of the symmetric energy tensor $(T_\mu^{\ \nu})$, which will have the necessary properties.

The case in which L depends on a scalar function, U, and its first derivatives $(\partial U/\partial x^\mu)$ will be examined first. In this case

$$\delta L = \frac{\partial L}{\partial U}\delta U + \frac{\partial L}{\partial\left(\dfrac{\partial U}{\partial x^\mu}\right)}\delta\left(\frac{\partial U}{\partial x^\mu}\right). \tag{4.4}$$

Since U is a scalar quantity by definition $\delta U = 0$. The formula for transformation of $(\partial U/\partial x^\mu)$ is:

$$\frac{\partial U'}{\partial x'^\mu} = \frac{\partial x^\nu}{\partial x'^\mu}\frac{\partial U}{\partial x^\nu}.$$

From (4.2), written in the form

$$x'^\nu = x^\nu + a^\nu_{\ \lambda}x^\lambda,$$

$$\frac{\partial x'^\nu}{\partial x'^\mu} = \frac{\partial x^\nu}{\partial x'^\mu} + a^\nu_{\ \lambda}\frac{\partial x^\lambda}{\partial x'^\mu},$$

i.e.

$$\frac{\partial x^\nu}{\partial x'^\mu} = \delta^\nu_{\ \mu} - a^\nu_{\ \lambda}\frac{\partial x^\lambda}{\partial x'^\mu}$$

$$= \delta^\nu_{\ \mu} - a^\nu_{\ \lambda}\left(\delta^\lambda_{\ \mu} \quad a^\lambda_{\ \rho}\frac{\partial x^\rho}{\partial x'^\lambda}\right)$$

$$= \delta^\nu_{\ \mu} - a^\nu_{\ \mu} \tag{4.5}$$

to the first order of small quantities.

Thus

$$\frac{\partial U'}{\partial x'^\mu} = \frac{\partial U}{\partial x^\mu} - a^\nu{}_\mu \frac{\partial U}{\partial x^\nu}$$

or

$$\delta\left(\frac{\partial U}{\partial x^\mu}\right) = -a^\nu{}_\mu \frac{\partial U}{\partial x^\nu}, \tag{4.6}$$

where the change in the differential coefficient as a result of the transformation, denoted by $\delta(\partial U/\partial x^\mu)$, is equal to

$$\left(\frac{\partial U'}{\partial x'^\mu} - \frac{\partial U}{\partial x^\mu}\right).$$

Thus

$$\delta L = -a^\nu{}_\mu \frac{\partial U}{\partial x^\nu} \frac{\partial L}{\partial\left(\dfrac{\partial U}{\partial x^\mu}\right)}.$$

This can be written in the form:

$$\delta L = a^\nu{}_\mu t_\nu{}^\mu$$

with

$$t_\nu{}^\mu = -\frac{\partial L}{\partial\left(\dfrac{\partial U}{\partial x^\mu}\right)} \frac{\partial U}{\partial x^\nu}, \tag{4.7}$$

the negative sign being of no significance, since it might have be incorporated in $a^\nu{}_\mu$.

In this case, according to equation (3.33), the energy tensor is already symmetrical for it is

$$\Theta^\mu{}_\nu = \frac{\partial L}{\partial\left(\dfrac{\partial U}{\partial x^\mu}\right)} \frac{\partial U}{\partial x^\nu} - \gamma^\mu{}_\nu L.$$

The first term on the right hand has just been shown to be symmetrical and the second term has the same property since $\gamma^\mu{}_\nu = \gamma_\nu{}^\mu$.

As an example suppose that

$$L = \tfrac{1}{2}\gamma^{\alpha\beta} \frac{\partial U}{\partial x^\alpha} \frac{\partial U}{\partial x^\beta},$$

and consider the covariant form of $(\Theta^\mu{}_\nu)$, i.e.

$$\Theta_{\mu\nu} = \gamma_{\mu\lambda} \frac{\partial L}{\partial\left(\dfrac{\partial U}{\partial x^\lambda}\right)} \frac{\partial U}{\partial x^\nu} - \gamma_{\mu\nu} L.$$

Since

$$\frac{\partial L}{\partial\left(\dfrac{\partial U}{\partial x^\lambda}\right)} = \gamma^{\lambda\beta}\frac{\partial U}{\partial x^\beta}$$

$$\Theta_{\mu\nu} = \frac{\partial U}{\partial x^\mu}\frac{\partial U}{\partial x^\nu} - \gamma_{\mu\nu}L$$

and this is clearly symmetrical.

Next let it be supposed that L is a function of vector components (U_μ) and of their differential coefficients $(\partial U_\mu/\partial x^\nu)$. In this case

$$\delta L = \frac{\partial L}{\partial U_\mu}\delta U_\mu + \frac{\partial L}{\partial\left(\dfrac{\partial U_\mu}{\partial x^\nu}\right)}\delta\left(\frac{\partial U_\mu}{\partial x^\nu}\right).$$

Then $\qquad U'_\mu = \dfrac{\partial x^\nu}{\partial x'^\mu}U_\nu = (\delta^\nu{}_\mu - a^\nu{}_\mu)U_\nu = U_\mu - a^\nu{}_\mu U_\nu$

so that $\qquad\qquad\qquad \delta U_\mu = -a^\nu{}_\mu U_\nu,$ \hfill (4.8)

also $\qquad \dfrac{\partial U'_\mu}{\partial x'^\nu} = \dfrac{\partial}{\partial x^\lambda}(U_\mu + \delta U_\mu)\dfrac{\partial x^\lambda}{\partial x'^\nu}$

$$= \frac{\partial}{\partial x^\lambda}(U_\mu - a^\rho{}_\mu U_\rho)(\delta^\lambda{}_\nu - a^\lambda{}_\nu)$$

$$= \frac{\partial U_\mu}{\partial x^\nu} - a^\lambda{}_\nu\frac{\partial U_\mu}{\partial x^\lambda} - a^\rho{}_\mu\frac{\partial U_\rho}{\partial x^\nu}$$

i.e. $\qquad\qquad \delta\left(\dfrac{\partial U_\mu}{\partial x^\nu}\right) = -a^\lambda{}_\nu\dfrac{\partial U_\mu}{\partial x^\lambda} - a^\rho{}_\mu\dfrac{\partial U_\rho}{\partial x^\nu}.$

Thus

$$\delta L = -a^\nu{}_\mu U_\nu\frac{\partial L}{\partial U_\mu} - \left(a^\lambda{}_\nu\frac{\partial U_\mu}{\partial x^\lambda} + a^\rho{}_\mu\frac{\partial U_\rho}{\partial x^\nu}\right)\frac{\partial L}{\partial\left(\dfrac{\partial U_\mu}{\partial x^\nu}\right)}$$

$$= -a^\nu{}_\mu\left(U_\nu\frac{\partial L}{\partial U_\mu} + \frac{\partial U_\lambda}{\partial x^\nu}\frac{\partial L}{\partial\left(\dfrac{\partial U_\lambda}{\partial x^\mu}\right)} + \frac{\partial U_\nu}{\partial x^\lambda}\frac{\partial L}{\partial\left(\dfrac{\partial U_\mu}{\partial x^\lambda}\right)}\right).$$

By making use of Lagrange's equation:

$$\frac{\partial}{\partial x^\lambda}\frac{\partial L}{\partial\left(\dfrac{\partial U_\mu}{\partial x^\lambda}\right)} - \frac{\partial L}{\partial U_\mu} = 0,$$

the expression in the bracket can be put into the form:

$$\frac{\partial}{\partial x^\lambda}\left(U_\nu \frac{\partial L}{\partial\left(\frac{\partial U_\mu}{\partial x^\lambda}\right)}\right) + \frac{\partial U_\lambda}{\partial x^\nu}\frac{\partial L}{\partial\left(\frac{\partial U_\lambda}{\partial x^\mu}\right)}\cdot$$

It thus follows that

$$t_\nu{}^\mu = \frac{\partial}{\partial x^\lambda}\left(U_\nu \frac{\partial L}{\partial\left(\frac{\partial U_\mu}{\partial x^\lambda}\right)}\right) + \frac{\partial U_\lambda}{\partial x^\nu}\frac{\partial L}{\partial\left(\frac{\partial U_\lambda}{\partial x^\mu}\right)}$$

is symmetric.

In this case (cf. 3.69)

$$\Theta^\mu{}_\nu = \frac{\partial L}{\partial\left(\frac{\partial U_\lambda}{\partial x^\mu}\right)}\frac{\partial U_\lambda}{\partial x^\nu} - \gamma^\mu{}_\nu L$$

omitting dependence upon $(\partial U_\mu^*/\partial x^\nu)$.

Thus if

$$Z^\mu{}_\nu = \frac{\partial}{\partial x^\lambda}\left(U_\nu \frac{\partial L}{\partial\left(\frac{\partial U_\mu}{\partial x^\lambda}\right)}\right),$$

the tensor

$$T^\mu{}_\nu = \Theta^\mu{}_\nu + Z^\mu{}_\nu \tag{4.9}$$

is symmetric.

$(T^\mu{}_\nu)$ will be conserved if $\partial Z^\mu{}_\nu/\partial x^\mu$ vanishes for it is known that

$$\frac{\partial \Theta^\mu{}_\nu}{\partial x^\mu} = 0.$$

Suppose that a function $H^{\lambda\mu}{}_\nu$ exists, which is antisymmetric in λ and μ, i.e. $H^{\lambda\mu}{}_\nu = -H^{\mu\lambda}{}_\nu$. If

$$Z^\mu{}_\nu = \frac{\partial H^{\lambda\mu}{}_\nu}{\partial x^\lambda}, \tag{4.10}$$

$$\frac{\partial Z^\mu{}_\nu}{\partial x^\mu} = \frac{\partial^2 H^{\lambda\mu}{}_\nu}{\partial x^\mu\,\partial x^\lambda} = 0,$$

on account of the antisymmetry of $H^{\lambda\mu}{}_\nu$ in λ and μ.

In the present case

$$H^{\lambda\mu}{}_\nu = \frac{\partial L}{\partial\left(\frac{\partial U_\mu}{\partial x^\lambda}\right)} U_\nu \tag{4.11}$$

and if this expression is antisymmetric in λ and μ, the symmetric tensor $(T^\mu{}_\nu)$ is conserved.

For the sake of brevity the functions (U_μ) have been regarded as real, but in cases where the fifth coordinate is used they must be complex in this coordinate since $\partial/\partial x^5 = ik$. It is then necessary to consider L as dependent on (U_μ) and (U^*_μ). It follows from the structure of $(Z^\mu{}_\nu)$ that it is then independent of the fifth coordinate and so also is $(H^{\lambda\mu}{}_\nu)$. Thus the energy remains the same whether the density is taken to be $T^4{}_4$ or $\Theta^4{}_4$, since

$$Z^4{}_4 = \frac{\partial H^{k4}{}_4}{\partial x^k}.$$

The antisymmetry property makes $H^{44}{}_4$ vanish and $(\partial/\partial x^5)H^{54}{}_4$ being zero.

The integral of $Z^4{}_4$ throughout space vanishes, since it is supposed that the functions vanish at the boundaries of integration. It is thus possible to adopt $(T^\mu{}_\nu)$ as the energy tensor.

In the case under consideration the antisymmetry of $(H^{\lambda\mu}{}_\nu)$ in λ and μ requires that:

$$\frac{\partial L}{\partial\left(\dfrac{\partial U_\mu}{\partial x^\lambda}\right)}U_\nu = -\frac{\partial L}{\partial\left(\dfrac{\partial U_\lambda}{\partial x^\mu}\right)}U_\nu$$

and this is satisfied if L contains the differential coefficients in the form

$$\left(\frac{\partial U_\mu}{\partial x^\lambda} - \frac{\partial U_\lambda}{\partial x^\mu}\right).$$

This is the case in the electromagnetic theory where L contains the product $B^{\mu\nu}B_{\mu\nu}$, with

$$B_{\mu\nu} = \frac{\partial U_\nu}{\partial x^\mu} - \frac{\partial U_\mu}{\partial x^\nu},$$

(U_μ) denoting the electromagnetic vector potential.

As an example consider the case of an electromagnetic field in empty space.

$$L = -\tfrac{1}{4}B^{\mu\nu}B_{\mu\nu} = -\tfrac{1}{4}\gamma^{\mu\alpha}\gamma^{\nu\beta}B_{\alpha\beta}B_{\mu\nu}$$

$$\frac{\partial L}{\partial\left(\dfrac{\partial U_\rho}{\partial x^\sigma}\right)} = B^{\rho\sigma}$$

$$\Theta^\mu{}_\nu = \frac{\partial L}{\partial\left(\frac{\partial U_\lambda}{\partial x^\mu}\right)}\frac{\partial U_\lambda}{\partial x^\nu} - \gamma^\mu{}_\nu L = B^{\lambda\mu}\frac{\partial U_\lambda}{\partial x^\nu} - \delta^\mu{}_\nu L$$

$$Z^\mu{}_\nu = \frac{\partial}{\partial x^\lambda}\left(U_\nu \frac{\partial L}{\partial\left(\frac{\partial U_\mu}{\partial x^\lambda}\right)}\right) = U_\nu \frac{\partial B^{\mu\lambda}}{\partial x^\lambda} + B^{\mu\lambda}\frac{\partial U_\nu}{\partial x^\lambda}.$$

The field equations

$$\frac{\partial}{\partial x^\sigma}\left(\frac{\partial L}{\partial\left(\frac{\partial U_\rho}{\partial x^\sigma}\right)}\right) - \frac{\partial L}{\partial U} = 0$$

are in this case

$$\frac{\partial B^{\rho\sigma}}{\partial x^\sigma} = 0.$$

Thus

$$Z^\mu{}_\nu = B^{\mu\lambda}\frac{\partial U_\nu}{\partial x^\lambda},$$

so that

$$T^\mu{}_\nu = \Theta^\mu{}_\nu + Z^\mu{}_\nu = B^{\lambda\mu}\frac{\partial U_\lambda}{\partial x^\nu} - \delta^\mu{}_\nu L + B^{\mu\lambda}\frac{\partial U_\nu}{\partial x^\lambda}$$

$$= B^{\lambda\mu}B_{\nu\lambda} - \delta^\mu{}_\nu L.$$

The expression for $H^{\lambda\mu}{}_\nu$ in this case is by (4.11) $B^{\mu\lambda}U_\nu$ and the condition of antisymmetry in λ and μ is satisfied since $B^{\mu\lambda} = -B^{\lambda\mu}$.

If is further necessary to consider the case when the Lagrange function depends on a spinor quantity ψ. This is the function which occurs in the relativistic form of the quantum theory associated with the Dirac matrices ($\alpha_x, \alpha_y, \alpha_z$ and β). Dirac's equation in the case in which the electromagnetic field is absent is

$$\alpha_x\frac{\partial\psi}{\partial x} + \alpha_y\frac{\partial\psi}{\partial y} + \alpha_z\frac{\partial\psi}{\partial z} + \alpha_0\frac{\partial\psi}{c\,\partial t} + \frac{2\pi i}{h}M_0 c\beta\psi = 0. \qquad (4.12)$$

In the usual form the matrix $(-\alpha_0)$ is placed equal to the unit matrix. M_0 denotes the mass of the particle to which the equation applies.

If ψ^+ is the spinor conjugate to ψ, the four quantities

$$\psi^+\alpha_x\psi, \quad \psi^+\alpha_y\psi, \quad \psi^+\alpha_z\psi, \quad -\psi^+\alpha^4\psi,$$

are the components of a four-vector where α_4 replaces $i\alpha_0$ while $\psi^+\beta\psi$ is a scalar quantity.

The vector is a contravariant vector and the components should strictly be written in the form $\psi^+ \alpha^m \psi$, where m can take the values $(1, 2, 3, 4)$.

For the purposes of the quantum theory the matrices have constant components and the term relativistic means relativistic in the sense of the special theory of relativity. In the problems with which, at present, the theory is concerned gravitation plays no appreciable part. A quantum theory within the frame of the general theory has not yet been completely worked out and so far does not appear to be necessary. Some attempts have been made in this direction but the work and expressions developed are complicated.

Here the notation of the general theory of relativity will be preserved when it is possible to do so especially as in the five-dimensional theory, where the electromagnetic field appears in a way similar to that of gravitation, it is not always possible to banish the fields altogether.

In extending the theory to five dimensions, five matrices (γ^μ) will be introduced. In Dirac's theory the parameter t is distinguished in that in the equation $\partial\psi / c\,\partial t$ is multiplied by the unit matrix.

In the present theory the equation is written in the form

$$\gamma^\mu \frac{\partial \psi}{\partial x^\mu} = 0 \tag{4.13}$$

so that in the absence of the fields, bearing in mind that ψ also now contains x^5 in the factor e^{ikx^5} and in no other way, this equation becomes:

$$\frac{\gamma^l}{\partial x^l}\frac{\partial \psi}{} + \frac{\gamma^4}{i} \frac{\partial \psi}{c\,\partial t} + ik\,\gamma^5 \psi = 0.$$

l having the values 1, 2, 3.

The special feature of Dirac's equation is the occurrence of the unit matrix with the term containing $\partial \psi / \partial t$. This gives a special significance to the parameter t which it is here necessary to avoid. In the calculus associated with Dirac's work the functions ψ and its conjugate function ψ^+ are used to determine average values of quantities represented by operators. Thus $c\alpha_x$ is the velocity operator in the x-direction and the value of the velocity is $\psi^+ c\alpha_x \psi$.

With the symmetrical introduction of five matrices (γ^μ) this average value will be represented by $\theta^+ c\gamma^\mu \psi$ and just as $\psi^+ \alpha^m \psi$ is a component of a contravariant four-vector so $\theta^+ \gamma^\mu \psi$ is a component of a five-vector. But $\theta^+\gamma^m\psi$ $(m=1,2,3,4)$ will be identified with $-\psi^+\alpha^m\psi$. Thus θ^+ will be placed equal to $\psi^+i\gamma$, where γ is a matrix with constant components and

$$-i\gamma\gamma^k = \alpha^k$$

in the case when Dirac's equation applies, i.e. in the absence of a gravitational field when the matrices (γ^m,γ_5) are constants.

In this case $-i\gamma\gamma^4$ must be equal to $+i$ multiplied by the unit matrix so that γ has the value taken by γ^4 when its components are constant. It is convenient to complete the relations for the matrices (α^m) by writing $\alpha^4 = -i\gamma\gamma^4 = -i$.

In the general case the matrices (γ^μ) are dependent on the co-ordinates, but they become constant when there is no gravitational field except γ^5 which is equal to $[(\gamma_5/\gamma_{55})-\alpha\phi_m\gamma^m]$, ϕ_m being a component of the electromagnetic field and γ_5 being always constant. It will be seen that $-i\gamma\gamma_5/\sqrt{(\gamma_{55})}$ must be identified with β.

The matrices (γ^μ) are introduced in the adoption of a line element matrix

$$ds = \gamma_\mu dx^\mu \qquad (4.14)$$

where the matrices γ_μ are defined by the relations

$$\gamma_\mu = \gamma_{\mu\nu}\gamma^\nu.$$

The idea associated with the introduction of this expression is that it may be possible to discover in geometry a further unifying concept which will show the relation of the phenomena of the microscopic to those of the macroscopic world.

The notation will be developed at a later stage. Only a limited introduction is now necessary to show how a symmetric energy tensor can be obtained when the Lagrange function depends upon a spinor quantity and its first differential coefficient.

The five matrices (γ^μ) are assumed to satisfy the relations:

$$\gamma^\mu\gamma^\nu+\gamma^\nu\gamma^\mu = 2\gamma^{\mu\nu}. \qquad (4.15)$$

This is a generalization of Dirac's relations:

$$\alpha^l\alpha^k+\alpha^k\alpha^l = 2\delta^{lk}, \quad \alpha^l\beta+\beta\alpha^l = 0.$$

The generalization appears to have been introduced by Tetrode for a four-dimensional continuum in which case the coefficients (g^{mn}) replace $(\gamma^{\mu\nu})$.

With the notation

$$\gamma_\mu = \gamma_{\mu\nu}\gamma^\nu, \quad \gamma^\mu = \gamma^{\mu\nu}\gamma_\nu, \tag{4.16}$$

it follows from (4.15) that

and

$$\left.\begin{array}{l} \gamma_\mu\gamma^\nu + \gamma^\nu\gamma_\mu = 2\gamma_\mu{}^\nu \quad (\text{or } 2\delta_\mu{}^\nu) \\[2mm] \gamma_\mu\gamma_\nu + \gamma_\nu\gamma_\mu = 2\gamma_{\mu\nu}. \end{array}\right\} \tag{4.17}$$

It thus appears that the square of the line matrix

$$(ds)^2 = \gamma_{\mu\nu}\,dx^\mu\,dx^\nu,$$

from which it follows that the proper value of the line matrix is the familiar line element of Riemannian geometry. Thus Tetrode's relation can be regarded as the link between the microscopic and the macroscopic world.

The symmetric part of $\gamma^\mu\gamma^\nu$ is the coefficient $\gamma^{\mu\nu}$ and the anti-symmetric part is denoted by $s^{\mu\nu}$. Thus

$$2s^{\mu\nu} = \gamma^\mu\gamma^\nu - \gamma^\nu\gamma^\mu. \tag{4.18}$$

When the matrices are constants components of $s^{\mu\nu}$ are equal to products of the Dirac matrices, e.g. $s^{12} = \alpha_x\alpha_y$. A useful relation is

$$s^{\mu\nu}\gamma^\lambda - \gamma^\lambda s^{\mu\nu} = 2(\gamma^{\lambda\nu}\gamma^\mu - \gamma^{\lambda\mu}\gamma^\nu), \tag{4.19}$$

which follows from the equation (4.15).

For the present purpose of finding a suitable energy tensor the matrices are assumed to be constant, undergoing no change with the infinitesimal transformation.

It is required to find the changes $\delta\psi$ and $\delta(\partial\psi/\partial x^\mu)$ resulting from this transformation.

Since $\theta^+\gamma^\mu\psi$ is a vector component,

$$\delta(\theta^+\gamma^\mu\psi) = a^\mu{}_\nu\theta^+\gamma^\nu\psi$$

in accordance with the rule of transformation of a contravariant vector (4.2), i.e.

$$x'^\mu - x^\mu = \delta x^\mu = a^\mu{}_\nu x^\nu.$$

Thus it is necessary that

$$\delta\theta^+\gamma^\mu\psi + \theta^+\gamma^\mu\delta\psi = a^\mu{}_\nu\theta^+\gamma^\nu\psi$$

and this can be satisfied by

$$\delta\theta^+ = \tfrac{1}{4}a_{\lambda\rho}\theta^+ s^{\rho\lambda}, \quad \delta\psi = \tfrac{1}{4}a_{\lambda\rho}s^{\lambda\rho}\psi.$$

This may be verified by substitution in (4.19) as follows:

$$\tfrac{1}{4}a_{\lambda\rho}\,\theta^+(s^{\rho\lambda}\gamma^\mu+\gamma^\mu s^{\lambda\rho})\,\psi = \tfrac{1}{4}a_{\lambda\rho}\,\theta^+(s^{\rho\lambda}\gamma^\mu-\gamma^\mu s^{\rho\lambda})\,\psi$$

$$= \tfrac{1}{2}a_{\lambda\rho}\,\theta^+(\gamma^{\mu\lambda}\gamma^\rho-\gamma^{\mu\rho}\gamma^\lambda)\,\psi$$

by means of the relation (4.18).

This may then be written in the form:

$$\tfrac{1}{2}(a^\mu{}_\rho\,\theta^+\gamma^\rho\,\psi-a_\chi{}^\mu\,\theta^+\gamma^\lambda\,\psi) = a^\mu{}_\nu\,\theta^+\gamma^\nu\,\psi.$$

The change

$$\delta\left(\frac{\partial\psi}{\partial x^\mu}\right) = \frac{\partial}{\partial x^\mu}(\delta\psi)$$

$$= \frac{\partial\psi'}{\partial x'^\mu}-\frac{\partial\psi}{\partial x^\mu}$$

$$= \frac{\partial}{\partial x^\nu}(\psi+\delta\psi)\frac{\partial x^\nu}{\partial x'^\mu}-\frac{\partial\psi}{\partial x^\mu}.$$

On substitution of the expression for $\delta\psi$ from (4.20) and making use of (4.5), it follows that

$$\delta\left(\frac{\partial\psi}{\partial x^\mu}\right) = -a^\nu{}_\mu\frac{\partial\psi}{\partial x^\nu}+\tfrac{1}{4}a_{\lambda\rho}s^{\lambda\rho}\frac{\partial\psi}{\partial x^\mu},$$

similarly

$$\delta\left(\frac{\partial\theta^+}{\partial x^\mu}\right) = -a^\nu{}_\mu\frac{\partial\theta^+}{\partial x^\nu}+\tfrac{1}{4}a_{\lambda\rho}\frac{\partial\theta^+}{\partial x^\mu}s^{\rho\lambda}. \qquad(4.21)$$

Thus if

$$L = L\left(\psi,\,\theta^+,\,\frac{\partial\psi}{\partial x^\mu},\,\frac{\partial\theta^+}{\partial x^\mu}\right),$$

$$\delta L =\frac{\partial L}{\partial\psi}\delta\psi+\delta\theta^+\frac{\partial L}{\partial\theta^+}+\frac{\partial L}{\partial\left(\dfrac{\partial\psi}{\partial x^\mu}\right)}\delta\left(\frac{\partial\psi}{\partial x^\mu}\right)+\delta\left(\frac{\partial\theta^+}{\partial x^\mu}\right)\frac{\partial L}{\partial\left(\dfrac{\partial\theta^+}{\partial x^\mu}\right)}$$

ψ and θ^+ being regarded as independent in the variation. The place of

$$\delta\theta^+ \quad\text{and}\quad \delta\left(\frac{\partial\theta^+}{\partial x^\mu}\right)$$

before

$$\frac{\partial L}{\partial\theta^+} \quad\text{and}\quad \frac{\partial L}{\partial\left(\dfrac{\partial\theta^+}{\partial x^\mu}\right)}$$

is in accordance with the notation of spinor and matrix multiplication.

On substitution for the terms in $\delta\psi$ and $\delta(\partial\psi/\partial x^\mu)$ by means of the relations (4.20) and (4.21) the result obtained is

$$a_{\lambda\rho}\left\{\gamma^{\nu\rho}\frac{\partial L}{\partial\left(\dfrac{\partial\psi}{\partial x^\lambda}\right)}\frac{\partial\psi}{\partial x^\nu}+\frac{1}{4}\frac{\partial L}{\partial\psi}s^{\lambda\rho}\psi+\frac{1}{4}\frac{\partial L}{\partial\left(\dfrac{\partial\psi}{\partial x^\mu}\right)}s^{\lambda\rho}\frac{\partial\psi}{\partial x^\mu}\right\}$$

and from the field equation

$$\frac{\partial}{\partial x^\mu}\frac{\partial L}{\partial\left(\dfrac{\partial\psi}{\partial x^\mu}\right)}-\frac{\partial L}{\partial\psi}=0$$

this expression may be written as

$$a_{\lambda\rho}\left[\gamma^{\nu\rho}\frac{\partial L}{\partial\left(\dfrac{\partial\psi}{\partial x^\lambda}\right)}\frac{\partial\psi}{\partial x^\nu}+\frac{1}{4}\frac{\partial}{\partial x^\mu}\left\{\frac{\partial L}{\partial\left(\dfrac{\partial\psi}{\partial x^\mu}\right)}s^{\lambda\rho}\psi\right\}\right].$$

In the same way the terms in $\delta\theta^+$ and $\delta(\partial\theta^+/\partial x^\mu)$ become

$$a_{\lambda\rho}\left[\gamma^{\nu\rho}\frac{\partial\theta^+}{\partial x^\nu}\frac{\partial L}{\partial\left(\dfrac{\partial\theta^+}{\partial x^\lambda}\right)}+\frac{1}{4}\frac{\partial}{\partial x^\mu}\left\{\theta^+s^{\rho\lambda}\frac{\partial L}{\partial\left(\dfrac{\partial\theta^+}{\partial x^\mu}\right)}\right\}\right].$$

Thus with

$$H^{\mu\lambda\rho}=\frac{1}{4}\left\{\frac{\partial L}{\partial\left(\dfrac{\partial\psi}{\partial x^\mu}\right)}s^{\lambda\rho}\psi+\theta^+s^{\rho\lambda}\frac{\partial L}{\partial\left(\dfrac{\partial\theta^+}{\partial x^\mu}\right)}\right\}\qquad(4.22)$$

and

$$Z^{\lambda\rho}=\frac{\partial H^{\mu\lambda\rho}}{\partial x^\mu},$$

the symmetric energy tensor is:

$$T^{\lambda\rho}=\gamma^{\nu\rho}\left\{\frac{\partial L}{\partial\left(\dfrac{\partial\psi}{\partial x^\lambda}\right)}\frac{\partial\psi}{\partial x^\nu}+\frac{\partial\theta^+}{\partial x^\nu}\frac{\partial L}{\partial\left(\dfrac{\partial\theta^+}{\partial x^\lambda}\right)}\right\}+Z^{\lambda\rho}-\gamma^{\lambda\rho}L.\qquad(4.23)$$

The case in which

$$L=A\left(\theta^+\gamma^\alpha\frac{\partial\psi}{\partial x^\alpha}-\frac{\partial\theta^+}{\partial x^\alpha}\gamma^\alpha\psi\right)\qquad(4.24)$$

illustrates the antisymmetric property of $H^{\mu\lambda\rho}$.

In order to obtain a suggestion for the form of a tensor to represent the angular momentum associated with a field let the case of a particle be considered. In this case the tensor

$$T^{\mu\nu} = \rho_0 \frac{dx^\mu}{d\tau} \frac{dx^\nu}{d\tau}$$

and this can be written in the form:

$$T^{\mu\nu} = \rho_0 \left(\frac{dt}{d\tau}\right)^2 \frac{dx^\mu}{dt} \frac{dx^\nu}{dt}.$$

ρ_0 is the proper density of the particle and $\rho_0(dt/d\tau)^2$ the ordinary density. The factor $(dt/d\tau)$ occurs twice, once in the introduction of ordinary mass, e.g. $m = m_0(dt/d\tau)$, and again in the volume element since $dx_0 = dx(dt/d\tau)$. Thus

$$T^{\mu\nu} = \rho \frac{\partial x^\mu}{dt} \frac{\partial x^\nu}{dt}$$

and in the case when $\mu = 4$,

$$T^{4\nu} = \rho i c \frac{dx^\nu}{dt}.$$

Thus the momentum density $\rho(dx^\nu/dt) = T^{4\nu}/ic$.

The angular moment density is

$$\rho \left(x^l \frac{dx^k}{dt} - x^k \frac{dx^l}{dt} \right)$$

where l and k can take the values 1, 2, 3. Thus in the case of a field for which the energy tensor is $(\Theta^{\mu\nu})$ the suggestion is that the angular momentum tensor might be defined as

$$M^{4\mu\nu} = (x^\mu \Theta^{4\nu} - x^\nu \Theta^{4\mu}).$$

It turns out however that this is not generally satisfactory. The attempt will be made to find a tensor which is conserved, i.e.

$$\frac{\partial M^{\lambda\mu\nu}}{\partial x^\lambda} = 0 \tag{4.25}$$

and which, in the case of a particle, agrees with the familiar definition of angular momentum.

The method of approach will be by variation of the integral $\int L\,d\omega$, where $d\omega$ is the five-dimensional volume element, when the co-ordinates are subjected to an infinitesimal Lorentz transformation

$$x'^{\mu} = x^{\mu} + a^{\mu}{}_{\nu}x^{\nu}$$

with

$$a^{\mu}{}_{\nu} = -a_{\nu}{}^{\mu}.$$

The variation considered will be

$$\delta \int L\,d\omega = \int L'\,d\omega' - \int L\,d\omega = 0.$$

From this it will be found possible to deduce the form of an invariant tensor $(M^{\lambda\mu\nu})$.

The function L will be considered to depend on a vector (U_{μ}) and its first differential coefficient $(\partial U_{\mu}/\partial x^{\nu})$, but not upon the coordinates explicitly.

The element $d\omega'$ resulting from a change of coordinates is

$$d\omega' = \left| \frac{\partial x'^{\alpha}}{\partial x^{\beta}} \right| d\omega$$

where $|\partial x'^{\alpha}/\partial x^{\beta}|$ denotes the determinant made up of terms $(\partial x'^{\alpha}/\partial x^{\beta})$.

This determinant takes a simple form for an infinitesimal transformation:

$$x'^{\alpha} = x^{\alpha} + \xi^{\alpha}$$

where ϵ is a quantity of the first order of small quantities. For

$$\frac{\partial x'^{\alpha}}{\partial x^{\beta}} = \delta^{\alpha}{}_{\beta} + \frac{\partial \xi^{\alpha}}{\partial x^{\beta}}$$

and if only the first power of ξ^{α} is retained the determinant reduces to the product of the diagonal terms, which to the first order is $[1 + (\partial\xi^{\alpha}/\partial x^{\alpha})]$, summed for α. Thus

$$L'\,d\omega' = \left(L'(x) + \frac{\partial L'}{\partial x^{\alpha}}\xi^{\alpha} \right)\left(1 + \frac{\partial \xi^{\alpha}}{\partial x^{\alpha}} \right) d\omega$$

$$= \left\{ L'(x) + \frac{\partial}{\partial x^{\alpha}}(L\xi^{\alpha}) \right\} d\omega.$$

Thus

$$\delta \int L\,d\omega = \int \left\{ L'(x^{\mu}) - L(x^{\mu}) + \frac{\partial}{\partial x^{\alpha}}(L\,\delta x^{\alpha}) \right\} d\omega.$$

The difference $\{L'(x^\mu) - L(x^\mu)\}$ must be distinguished from

$$\{L'(x'^\mu) - L(x^\mu)\}$$

which has been denoted by δL. It will be denoted by $\delta_0 L$, and consequently

$$\delta L - \delta_0 L = L'(x'^\mu) - L'(x^\mu) = \frac{\partial L}{\partial x^\alpha} \delta x^\alpha$$

to the first order. Thus

$$\delta \int L \, d\omega = \int \left\{ \delta_0 L + \frac{\partial}{\partial x^\alpha} (L \, \delta x^\alpha) \right\} d\omega$$

and, if the integral has a stationary value,

$$\delta_0 L + \frac{\partial}{\partial x^\alpha} (L \, \delta x^\alpha) = 0.$$

This result is equivalent to

$$\frac{\partial L}{\partial U_\mu} \delta_0 U_\mu + \frac{\partial L}{\partial \left(\dfrac{\partial U_\mu}{\partial x^\nu} \right)} \delta_0 \left(\frac{\partial U_\mu}{\partial x^\nu} \right) + \frac{\partial}{\partial x^\nu} (L \, \delta x^\nu) = 0$$

or, on substituting from the Lagrange equations,

$$\frac{\partial}{\partial x^\nu} \frac{\partial L}{\partial \left(\dfrac{\partial U_\mu}{\partial x^\nu} \right)} - \frac{\partial L}{\partial U_\mu} = 0,$$

$$\frac{\partial}{\partial x^\nu} \left\{ \frac{\partial L}{\partial \left(\dfrac{\partial U_\mu}{\partial x^\nu} \right)} \delta_0 U_\mu + L \, \delta x^\nu \right\} = 0. \qquad (4.26)$$

In this way the quantity in the bracket has been found and it is conserved.

From the definition of $\delta_0 U_\mu$ it follows that

$$\delta_0 U_\mu = \delta U_\mu - \frac{\partial U_\mu}{\partial x^\rho} \delta x^\rho$$

$$= a_\mu{}^\lambda U_\lambda - \frac{\partial U_\mu}{\partial x^\rho} a^\rho{}_\lambda x^\lambda \quad \text{(cf. 4.2 and 4.8).}$$

Thus on substitution the quantity in the bracket becomes:

$$a_\lambda{}^\rho \left\{ \frac{\partial L}{\partial \left(\frac{\partial U_\lambda}{\partial x^\nu} \right)} U_\rho + x^\lambda \left(\frac{\partial L}{\partial \left(\frac{\partial U_\mu}{\partial x^\nu} \right)} \frac{\partial U_\mu}{\partial x^\rho} - \delta_\nu{}^\rho L \right) \right\}$$

$$= a_\lambda{}^\rho \left\{ \frac{\partial L}{\partial \left(\frac{\partial U_\lambda}{\partial x^\nu} \right)} U_\rho + x^\lambda \Theta^\nu{}_\rho \right\} \quad \text{(cf. 3.69)}$$

$$= a_{\lambda\rho} \left\{ \frac{\partial L}{\partial \left(\frac{\partial U_\lambda}{\partial x^\nu} \right)} U^\rho + x^\lambda \Theta^{\nu\rho} \right\}.$$

From the definition of the tensor $H^{\lambda\mu}{}_\nu$ in equation (4.11) the expression becomes:

$$a_{\lambda\rho}(H^{\nu\lambda\rho} + x^\lambda \Theta^{\nu\rho}).$$

If now λ is taken to be $> \rho$ the expression can be put in the form:

$$a_{\lambda\rho}(H^{\nu\lambda\rho} + x^\lambda \Theta^{\nu\rho}) + a_{\rho\lambda}(H^{\nu\rho\lambda} + x^\rho \Theta^{\nu\lambda})$$
$$= a_{\lambda\rho}[x^\lambda \Theta^{\nu\rho} - x^\rho \Theta^{\nu\lambda} + H^{\nu\lambda\rho} - H^{\nu\rho\lambda}].$$

If $M^{\nu\lambda\rho}$ is placed equal to the expression in the bracket it follows that

$$a_{\lambda\rho} \frac{\partial M^{\nu\lambda\rho}}{\partial x^\nu} = 0$$

is a result of the assumption that $\int L d\omega$ has a stationary value. This result will be examined in the case where the coefficients $(\gamma_{\mu\nu})$ are equal to $(\delta_{\mu\nu})$ as in a Galilean system when, for example, $\Theta^{\mu\rho}$ can be placed equal to $\Theta^\nu{}_\rho$. For conservation

$$\frac{\partial M^{\nu\lambda\rho}}{\partial x^\nu} = 0, \tag{4.27}$$

where

$$M^{\nu\lambda\rho} = x^\lambda \Theta^{\nu\rho} - x^\rho \Theta^{\nu\lambda} + H^{\nu\lambda\rho} - H^{\nu\rho\lambda}. \tag{4.28}$$

Thus:

$$\frac{\partial M^{\nu\lambda\rho}}{\partial x^\nu} = \delta^\lambda{}_\nu \Theta^{\nu\rho} + x^\lambda \frac{\partial \Theta^{\nu\rho}}{\partial x^\nu} - \delta^\rho{}_\nu \Theta^{\nu\lambda} - x^\rho \frac{\partial \Theta^{\nu\lambda}}{\partial x^\nu} + \frac{\partial H^{\nu\lambda\rho}}{\partial x^\nu} - \frac{\partial H^{\nu\rho\lambda}}{\partial x^\nu}$$

and by means of equations (3.34), (4.9) and (4.10) the right-hand side becomes $(T^{\lambda\rho} - T^{\rho\lambda})$. Since $(T^{\lambda\rho})$ is symmetric the relation (4.27) is verified.

If $\Theta^{\nu\rho}$ be replaced by $[T^{\nu\rho}-(\partial H^{\sigma\nu\rho}/\partial x^\sigma)]$ the expression for $M^{\nu\lambda\rho}$ becomes:

$$M^{\nu\lambda\rho} = x^\lambda T^{\nu\rho} - x^\rho T^{\nu\lambda} - \frac{\partial}{\partial x^\sigma}(x^\lambda H^{\sigma\nu\rho} - x^\rho H^{\sigma\nu\lambda}). \qquad (4.29)$$

In the case in which $\nu=4$, σ cannot have this value since $(H^{\sigma\nu\rho})$ is antisymmetric, and on account of the structure of $(H^{\sigma\nu\rho})$ it does not contain the coordinate x^5 since, when the function (U_ν) is complex containing this coordinate in the form e^{ikx^5}, the form of $(H^{\sigma\nu\rho})$ replacing that of the expression (4.11) is

$$H^{\lambda\mu}{}_\nu = \frac{\partial L}{\partial\left(\dfrac{\partial U_\mu}{\partial x^\lambda}\right)}U^*{}_\nu + \frac{\partial L}{\partial\left(\dfrac{\partial U_\mu}{\partial x^\lambda}\right)}U^*{}_\nu$$

and this does not contain x^5.

Thus the component with $\nu=4$,

$$M^{4\lambda\rho} = x^\lambda T^{4\rho} - x^\rho T^{4\lambda} - \frac{\partial}{\partial x^k}(x^\lambda H^{k4\rho} - x^\rho H^{k4\lambda})$$

and on integration throughout the volume, provided that the quantities concerned vanish at the boundaries, the terms within the bracket make no contribution.

The angular momentum density can thus be represented in terms of the symmetric energy tensor as

$$M^{4\lambda\rho} = x^\lambda T^{4\rho} - x^\rho T^{4\lambda}. \qquad (4.30)$$

This then corresponds exactly to the expression considered for the case of the particle where, also, the energy tensor is symmetric and the angular momentum is obtained by dividing $M^{4\lambda\rho}$ by ic.

The angular momentum $(M^{4\lambda\rho})$ can be divided into two parts, the first of these being similar to the momentum of a particle moving in some orbit and depending on the origin of coordinates. This can be described as the angular momentum of the path or orbital angular momentum and is denoted by

$$R^{\lambda\rho} = x^\lambda \Theta^{4\rho} - x^\rho \Theta^{4\lambda}. \qquad (4.31)$$

The second part is independent of the origin of coordinates and is described by the term spin being denoted by

$$S^{\lambda\rho} = H^{4\lambda\rho} - H^{4\rho\lambda}. \qquad (4.32)$$

As an example of the expression for the spin angular momentum the case of the vector field, for which the Lagrangian is given by the expression (3.68), may be considered. The dependence of L on (U_λ), (U_λ^*) and their first differential coefficients gives

$$H^{\nu\lambda\rho} = \frac{\partial L}{\partial\left(\dfrac{\partial U_\lambda^*}{\partial x^\nu}\right)}\, U^{*\rho} + \frac{\partial L}{\partial\left(\dfrac{\partial U_\lambda}{\partial x^\nu}\right)}\, U^\rho$$

$$= \tfrac{1}{2}(V^{\nu\lambda}\, U^{*\rho} + V^{*\nu\lambda}\, U^\rho)$$

and the spin

$$H^{\nu\rho\lambda} - H^{\nu\lambda\rho} = \tfrac{1}{2}(V^{\lambda\nu}\, U^{*\rho} + V^{*\lambda\nu}\, U^\rho - V^{\rho\nu}\, U^{*\lambda} - V^{*\rho\nu}\, U^\lambda). \quad (4.33)$$

In the case of the scalar field the energy tensor $(\Theta^{\mu\nu})$ is symmetric and there is no spin term.

In many problems concerning the nuclear field it is possible to neglect the influence of the electromagnetic field as well as that of the gravitational field. When, however, the electromagnetic field has to be considered, terms representing it must appear in the Lagrange function, which becomes a function of the electromagnetic potential (ϕ_m) and of its first differential coefficient $(\partial\phi_m/\partial x^n)$. These functions depend only on four coordinates (x^n) and (ϕ_m) is a covariant four-vector. For the sake of uniformity it could be regarded as a five-vector with $\phi_5 = 0$. In this case the contravariant components are (ϕ^m, ϕ^5) with $\phi^5 = -\alpha\phi^m\phi_m$.

In the theory of relativity Einstein found it possible to represent the equations of the gravitational field in the Lagrangian form by means of a function depending upon the components (g^{mn}) and their first differential coefficients. His method may be followed in the case of the components $(\gamma_{\mu\nu})$ and their first differential coefficients and the electromagnetic equations should now be included in the system of equations derived. The way in which the electromagnetic quantities appear as a result of a particular choice of the line element has already been considered in Chapter 2, where it appears that they can be regarded as representing what may be described as a geometrical condition at each point where measurements are to be made. This is in agreement with the view of G. Mie that the emphasis in the theory is to be laid on concepts associated with the field and not upon currents and charge densities, the latter being manifestations of the more fundamental field intensities and quantities related to them.

The field theory of gravitation can be based upon the curvature function, R, of equation (2.97) taken as the Lagrange density function. The electromagnetic field equations can be derived by choosing the function, B, of that equation as the Lagrangian.

It will not be necessary to consider the influence of the field of gravitation in the present discussions so that, it is possible to adopt

$$L = -\tfrac{1}{4}B = -\tfrac{1}{4}B_{\mu\nu}B^{\mu\nu} \qquad (4.34)$$

for the purpose of deriving the field equations. Both the gravitational and electromagnetic equations derived in this way are those for empty space. They are valid for regions where there is no matter and no electricity.

Clearly L is a function of the differential coefficients $(\partial\phi_\nu/\partial x^\mu)$ but is independent of (ϕ_ν) itself. It is also supposed to be independent of the coordinates explicitly.

The field equations are of the type

$$\frac{\partial}{\partial x^\nu}\frac{\partial L}{\partial\left(\dfrac{\partial\phi_\mu}{\partial x^\nu}\right)} = 0.$$

Writing $L = -\tfrac{1}{4}\gamma^{\mu\rho}\gamma^{\nu\sigma}B_{\mu\nu}B_{\rho\sigma}$ it appears that

$$\frac{\partial L}{\partial\left(\dfrac{\partial\phi_\alpha}{\partial x^\beta}\right)} = B^{\alpha\beta} \qquad (4.35)$$

and the field equations are

$$\frac{\partial B^{\mu\nu}}{\partial x^\nu} = 0.$$

When a current is present, a current vector (J^μ) exists and the equation is:

$$\frac{\partial B^{\mu\nu}}{\partial x^\nu} = J^\mu. \qquad (4.36)$$

This is the case considered at the end of Chapter 2.

If this is to be derived from a Lagrangian function clearly L must be so constructed that

$$\frac{\partial L}{\partial\phi_\mu} = J^\mu$$

so that equation (4.36) is equal to

$$\frac{\partial}{\partial x^\nu} \frac{\partial L}{\partial \left(\dfrac{\partial \phi_\mu}{\partial x^\nu}\right)} - \frac{\partial L}{\partial \phi_\mu} = 0. \tag{4.37}$$

It occurs in some cases that there is interaction between an electromagnetic field and a field of another kind, the interaction being represented by the dependence of the Lagrangian for the second field upon the electromagnetic potential (ϕ_μ).

Suppose that the Lagrangian function depends on functions (θ_μ) and $(\delta\theta_\mu/\delta x^\nu)$ representing this field. The energy tensor

$$\Theta^\mu{}_\nu = \frac{\partial L}{\partial \left(\dfrac{\partial \theta_\alpha}{\partial x^\mu}\right)} \frac{\partial \theta_\alpha}{\partial x^\nu} - \delta^\mu{}_\nu L$$

is not now conserved owing to the dependence of L upon (ϕ_μ).

It is necessary to take account of the electromagnetic field since the interaction means an interchange of energy.

Suppose that $(E^\mu{}_\nu)$ denotes the energy tensor for the electromagnetic field:

$$E^\mu{}_\nu = B^{\rho\mu} B_{\nu\rho} + \tfrac{1}{4}\delta^\mu{}_\nu B$$

and this quantity is not conserved, in fact

$$\frac{\partial E^\mu{}_\nu}{\partial x^\mu} = J^\mu B_{\nu\mu}$$

according to the relativistic form of Maxwell's theory.

In the case of the electromagnetic theory μ, ν take the values 1 to 4, but these affixes may have the values 1 to 5 in the equations for other kinds of field. However, the structure of L and $(\Theta^\mu{}_\nu)$ is such that the fifth coordinate does not occur in them and the expression $\partial \Theta^\mu{}_\nu/\partial x^\mu$ can be written in the form $\partial \Theta^m{}_\nu/\partial x^m$, where m runs from 1 to 4.

On differentiating $\Theta^\mu{}_\nu$ and taking account of the field equations

$$\frac{\partial \Theta^\mu{}_\nu}{\partial x^\mu} = \frac{\partial}{\partial x^\mu} \frac{\partial L}{\partial \left(\dfrac{\partial \theta_\alpha}{\partial x^\mu}\right)} \frac{\partial \theta_\alpha}{\partial x^\nu} + \frac{\partial L}{\partial \left(\dfrac{\partial \theta_\alpha}{\partial x^\mu}\right)} \frac{\partial^2 \theta_\alpha}{\partial x^\mu \partial x^\nu}$$

$$- \delta^\mu{}_\nu \left\{ \frac{\partial L}{\partial \left(\dfrac{\partial \theta_\alpha}{\partial x^\beta}\right)} \frac{\partial^2 \theta_\alpha}{\partial x^\mu \partial x^\beta} + \frac{\partial L}{\partial \theta_\alpha} \frac{\partial \theta_\alpha}{\partial x^\mu} + \frac{\partial L}{\partial \phi_\alpha} \frac{\partial \phi_\alpha}{\partial x^\mu} \right\}$$

101

since L is a function of (ϕ_α). Thus

$$\frac{\partial \Theta^\mu_{\ \nu}}{\partial x^\mu} = -\frac{\partial L}{\partial \phi_\alpha}\frac{\partial \phi_\alpha}{\partial x^\nu}.$$

Since (ϕ_α) is independent of x^5,

$$\frac{\partial \Theta^\mu_{\ 5}}{\partial x^\mu} = \frac{\partial \Theta^m_{\ 5}}{\partial x^m} = 0 \tag{4.38}$$

and the quantity represented by $(\Theta^m_{\ 5})$ is conserved. In the case when $\nu = n$,

$$\frac{\partial \Theta^m_{\ n}}{\partial x^m} = -\frac{\partial L}{\partial \phi_l}\frac{\partial \phi_l}{\partial x^n}$$

where the affixes may have the values 1 to 4.

It has been seen that

$$\frac{\partial E^m_{\ n}}{\partial x^m} = +J^m B_{nm} = +J^m\left(\frac{\partial \phi_m}{\partial x^n} - \frac{\partial \phi_n}{\partial x^m}\right).$$

But $\partial J^m/\partial x^m = 0$ by the relation (4.36) since B^{mn} is antisymmetric in m and n. In other words the current (J^m) is conserved and consequently

$$\frac{\partial}{\partial x^m}(J^m \phi_n) = J^m\frac{\partial \phi_n}{\partial x^m}.$$

Thus

$$J^m\frac{\partial \phi_m}{\partial x^n} = \frac{\partial E^m_{\ n}}{\partial x^m} + \frac{\partial}{\partial x^m}(J^m \phi_n)$$

and

$$\frac{\partial}{\partial x^m}(\Theta^m_{\ n} + E^m_{\ n} + J^m \phi_n) = 0. \tag{4.39}$$

The total energy tensor is thus:

$$Q^m_{\ n} = \Theta^m_{\ n} + E^m_{\ n} + J^m \phi_n. \tag{4.40}$$

As a consequence of the law expressed by equation (2.110) and the special case of it by (2.113), it appears that

$$P^m_{\ 5} = \chi \Theta^m_{\ 5}$$

but by the relation (2.88),

$$P^m_{\ 5} = -\tfrac{1}{2}\gamma_{55}\,\alpha J^m,$$

where J^m is written for the current density. Thus

$$J^m = -\alpha \Theta^m{}_5, \tag{4.41}$$

since $\chi = \frac{1}{2}\gamma_{55}\alpha^2$, and the total energy tensor takes the form:

$$Q^m{}_n = \Theta^m{}_n - \alpha\phi_n \Theta^m{}_5 + E^m{}_n. \tag{4.42}$$

From the appropriate relation in equations (2.61), it will be seen that the first two terms on the right of equation (4.42) form the four-dimensional counterpart of $(\Theta^m{}_n)$.

Bibliography

1. w. PAULI, 1921. *Relativitäts-Theorie*, § 23. B. G. Teubner.
   w. PAULI, 1941. *Rev. mod. Phys.* **13** (3), 203.
2. F. HUND, 1954. *Materie als Feld*. Kap. IX. Springer.
3. F. BELINFANTE, 1939. *Physica*, **6**, 887.

CHAPTER 5

The Derivation of the First-Order Quantum Equation

In the last chapter, in considering the formation of a symmetric energy tensor in the case when the Lagrange function depends upon a spinor quantity, a set of matrices (γ^μ) was introduced and their relation to the Dirac matrices was examined. Before proceeding to the main object of the present chapter the corresponding set of matrices $(\beta^m, \beta.)$ appropriate in four dimensions is introduced and its properties deduced. In the presence of a gravitational field they are regarded as dependent upon the coordinates but are constant in the absence of this field. In the latter case they are related to the Dirac matrices.

The form of the relations between the γ- and β-matrices is assumed to be similar to that which exists between the four- and five-vector components. Thus

$$\gamma^m = \beta^m, \quad \gamma_5 = \sqrt{(\gamma_{55})}\,\beta. \tag{5.1}$$

By means of the relations (4.16) it follows that

$$\gamma^5 = \frac{\gamma_5}{\gamma_{55}} - \frac{\gamma_{5m}}{\gamma_{55}}\gamma^m = \frac{\beta.}{\sqrt{(\gamma_{55})}} - \alpha\phi_m\beta^m. \tag{5.2}$$

It follows also from (4.16) that $\gamma_m = \gamma_{m\mu}\gamma^\mu$ so that

$$\gamma_m = g_{mn}\beta^n + \sqrt{(\gamma_{55})}\,\alpha\phi_m\beta. \tag{5.3}$$

If now $$\beta_m = g_{mn}\beta^n, \tag{5.4}$$

$$\gamma_m = \beta_m + \sqrt{(\gamma_{55})}\,\alpha\phi_m\beta. \quad \text{(cf. 2.60).}$$

Moreover from the relations (4.17) it may be shown that

$$\left.\begin{array}{l} \beta^m\beta. + \beta.\,\beta^m = 0, \\ \beta_m\beta^n + \beta^n\beta_m = 2\delta_m{}^n, \\ \beta_m\beta_n + \beta_n\beta_m = 2g_{mn}, \\ \beta^m\beta^n + \beta^n\beta^m = 2g^{mn}. \end{array}\right\} \tag{5.5}$$

It is convenient to record the values of these matrices when the components are constant. β^1, β^2, β^3, β^4 and β. can be obtained from the matrix

$$
\begin{bmatrix}
-z & -x+iy & +iu+v & 0 \\
-x-iy & z & 0 & iu+v \\
-iu+v & 0 & z & x-iy \\
0 & -iu+v & x+iy & -z
\end{bmatrix}
\tag{5.6}
$$

To obtain β^1 the value of x is placed equal to unity and the other letters are placed equal to zero. To obtain β^2 the value of y is placed equal to unity and the remaining letters equal to zero and similarly for the other matrices.

The values of α^1, α^2 and α^3 or α_x, α_y and α_z can be obtained from the matrix

$$
\begin{bmatrix}
k & 0 & n & l-im \\
0 & k & l+im & -n \\
n & l-im & -k & 0 \\
l+im & -n & 0 & -k
\end{bmatrix}
\tag{5.7}
$$

α^1 is obtained by writing $l=1$ and placing the other letters equal to zero, similarly for α^2 and α^3, while β is obtained by placing $l=m=n=0$ and $k=1$.

Useful relations are:

$$
\left.
\begin{aligned}
&\beta^1 = i\beta\alpha^2\alpha^3, \quad \beta^2 = i\beta\alpha^3\alpha^1, \quad \beta^3 = i\beta\alpha^1\alpha^2, \\
&\beta^4 = -\alpha^1\alpha^2\alpha^3\beta, \quad \beta. = \beta^1\beta^2\beta^3\beta^4 = -i\alpha^1\alpha^2\alpha^3, \\
&\alpha^k = -i\beta^4\beta^k, \, (k=1,2,3), \quad \alpha^4 = -i, \quad \beta = -i\beta_4\beta..
\end{aligned}
\right\}
\tag{5.8}
$$

It will be noted that in the absence of a gravitational field, but with the electromagnetic field present, the five-dimensional matrices are constructed linearly of constant matrices with variable coefficients (cf. 5.1, 5.2, 5.3). A representation of this character will be assumed in the general case, and later on the expression

$$
\gamma^\mu = h^\mu{}_\alpha E_\alpha
\tag{5.9}
$$

will be adopted for the form of a typical matrix γ^μ, the five matrices (E_α) being constant and the coefficients ($h^\mu{}_\alpha$) being dependent upon the coordinates.

It was pointed out in the introduction that the original derivation of Dirac's equation by an appeal to the principle of covariance left the equation isolated from the general background of physical theory in contrast to the law of gravitation which is indissolubly associated with it. The purpose now is to derive this equation in a way which portrays its intimate relation to the whole range of the phenomena of physics. The derivation depends upon the assumption that the matrices (γ^μ) depend upon the coordinates and that the appropriate line element of the continuum is

$$ds = \gamma_\mu \, dx^\mu \quad \text{(cf. 4.14).} \tag{5.10}$$

No attempt is made to develop a general relativistic theory of matrices, the fundamental assumptions lie in the adoption of the relations (5.9) and (5.10) and in the adoption of Tetrode's relation (4.15). The principle on which the derivation is based is that of H. Weyl described in Chapter 1 (cf. equation 1.19). The idea is that in the continuum a change of length may be associated with the parallel displacement of a vector. But the change of length must now apply to an expression based on the form of the matrix line element (5.10).

The matrix vector associated with an ordinary vector quantity (A^μ) is defined to be

$$A = \gamma_\mu A^\mu = \gamma^\mu A_\mu \tag{5.11}$$

and its matrix length L is defined as

$$L = \theta^+ A \psi, \tag{5.12}$$

where θ^+ and ψ are spinor quantities.

These are chosen to be spinor quantities because it is desired to relate this theory to the quantum theory. They can be regarded as gauging factors and are analogous to the factor λ^2 mentioned in connection with the theory of Weyl and Eddington in Chapter 1 (cf. equation 1.17). It will appear later that θ^+ is related to ψ, so that only one independent quantity is introduced in the gauging factor.

The parallel displacement adopted is Riemannian, that is to say that when a vector (A^μ) undergoes such a displacement the change in the components is defined by

$$\left.\begin{aligned} dA^\mu &= -\Delta^\mu_{\lambda\nu} A^\lambda \, dx^\nu, \\ dA_\mu &= \Delta^\lambda_{\mu\nu} A_\lambda \, dx^\nu, \end{aligned}\right\} \tag{5.13}$$

the coefficient $\Delta^\mu_{\lambda\nu}$ being defined by the expression (2.72). In this case the length, l, of a vector is unchanged since

$$dl^2 = d(\gamma_{\mu\nu} A^\mu A^\nu) = \left(\frac{\partial \gamma_{\mu\nu}}{\partial x^\lambda} - \gamma_{\rho\nu} \Delta^\rho_{\mu\lambda} - \gamma_{\mu\rho} \Delta^\rho_{\nu\lambda} \right) A^\mu A^\nu \, dx^\lambda$$

and the expression in brackets vanishes identically.

106

But the question now is: What change occurs in the matrix length, L, when the vector (A^μ) undergoes a Riemannian parallel displacement?

It is thus necessary to examine

$$dL = d(\theta^+ \gamma^\mu A_\mu \psi)$$

when the coordinates change from (x^μ) to $(x^\mu + dx^\mu)$ and A_μ changes by $\Delta^\lambda_{\mu\nu} A_\lambda dx^\nu$.

It follows that

$$dL = \left\{ \frac{\partial \theta^+}{\partial x^\lambda} \gamma^\mu \psi + \theta^+ \gamma^\mu \frac{\partial \psi}{\partial x^\lambda} + \theta^+ \left(\frac{\partial \gamma^\mu}{\partial x^\lambda} + \gamma^\rho \Delta^\mu_{\rho\lambda} \right) \psi \right\} A_\mu dx^\lambda.$$

The assumption made by Weyl was that the change in length was of the form: $dl = -l\phi_m dx^m$, i.e. it was linear in the changes of coordinates.

This suggests the assumption now that dL should take a similar form, and this would be

$$dL = \theta^+ R_\lambda \gamma^\mu A_\mu \psi dx^\lambda.$$

If the law of change is to be the same for all vectors and displacements the relation:

$$\frac{\partial \theta^+}{\partial x^\lambda} \gamma^\mu \psi + \theta^+ \gamma^\mu \frac{\partial \psi}{\partial x^\lambda} + \theta^+ K^\mu_\lambda \psi = \theta^+ R_\lambda \gamma^\mu \psi, \qquad (5.14)$$

where

$$K^\mu_\lambda = \frac{\partial \gamma^\mu}{\partial x^\lambda} + \gamma^\rho \Delta^\mu_{\rho\lambda}. \qquad (5.15)$$

The conditions imposed by the equation (5.14) are exacting and it is suggested that some simplification is necessary, if it is to represent a natural law.

The position before us is a reminder of that which confronted Einstein when he sought a relation which would express the law of gravitation. In this case he had before him the Riemann–Christoffel tensor $(B^\mu_{\lambda\sigma\rho})$ (cf. 1.14).

A simple limitation would have been obtained by placing this tensor equal to zero, but had this step been taken it would have destroyed the possibility of representing the phenomenon of gravitation by a geometrical approach since, if this tensor vanishes, the geometry is Euclidean (or Galilean). A less stringent requirement was therefore adopted, the limitation being upon the reduced tensor

$R_{\lambda\sigma} = \beta^{\mu}_{\lambda\sigma\mu}$, which in the early stage of the theory was placed equal to zero.

In the present consideration (K^{μ}_{λ}), composed of the fundamental matrices and the coefficients $(\Delta^{\mu}_{\rho\lambda})$, appears as the quantity corresponding to $(B^{\mu}_{\lambda\sigma\rho})$.

The first suggestion could be to place K^{μ}_{λ} equal to zero, but this is too exacting a condition for the present purpose and its adoption would defeat the object of the investigation. The form of the law of gravitation suggests the step to be taken, and it is apparent that the condition to be adopted is

$$K^{\mu}_{\mu} = 0. \tag{5.16}$$

Thus from equation (5.14),

$$\frac{\partial\theta^{+}}{\partial x^{\mu}}\gamma^{\mu}\psi + \theta^{+}\gamma^{\mu}\frac{\partial\psi}{\partial x^{\mu}} = \theta^{+}R_{\mu}\gamma^{\mu}\psi. \tag{5.17}$$

The appearance of the expression $\gamma^{\mu}(\partial\psi/\partial x^{\mu})$ (cf. equation 4.13) suggests a relation between the condition (5.17) and Dirac's equation, which is the fundamental equation of the quantum theory. It suggests that it should be interpreted as a law of gauging, the quantum theory thus appearing as a theory of measurement.

The function ψ is to be regarded as dependent upon x^{5}, containing this coordinate in the factor $\exp(ikx^{5})$. The constant k has already been interpreted in connection with field theories but it will now be considered by comparison of $\theta^{+}\gamma^{\mu}(\partial\psi/\partial x^{\mu})$ with Dirac's equation. The coordinate x^{5} is now to be regarded as occurring in the factor $e^{2\pi in'x^{5}/l_{0}}$, where n' is integral, positive or negative, and l_{0} is a fundamental length. Remembering that

$$\gamma^{5} = \frac{\gamma_{5}}{\gamma_{55}} - \alpha\phi_{m}\gamma^{m},$$

it follows that

$$\theta^{+}\gamma^{\mu}\frac{\partial\psi}{\partial x^{\mu}} = \theta^{+}\left\{\frac{\gamma^{4}}{i}\left(\frac{\partial}{\partial x^{0}} + 2\pi i\frac{n'\alpha}{l_{0}}\phi\right)\right.$$
$$\left. + \gamma^{k}\left(\frac{\partial}{\partial x^{k}} - 2\pi i\frac{n'\alpha}{l_{0}}\phi_{k}\right) + \frac{2\pi in'\gamma_{5}}{l_{0}\gamma_{55}}\right\}\psi, \tag{5.18}$$

where $x^{0} = ict$, and ϕ_{4} has been placed equal to $i\phi$.

In equation (2.54) the value of γ_{55} is given as $(n'/n)^{2}$ where the integer n' is the number of elementary charges, e, associated with the particle under consideration and nm_{0} denotes its mass.

In the relations (5.1) the matrix β. has been introduced for $\gamma_5/\sqrt{(\gamma_{55})}$.

Dirac's equation is usually written in the form:

$$\left(\frac{h}{2\pi i}\frac{\partial}{\partial x^0}+\frac{e}{c}\phi\right)\psi = \alpha^k\left(\frac{h}{2\pi i}\frac{\partial}{\partial x^k}-\frac{e}{c}\phi_k\right)\psi+M_0 c\beta\psi \qquad (5.19)$$

where e denotes the charge on the particle and M_0 is its mass.

In the notation of equation (5.18), e is replaced by $n'e$ where e is the charge of the electron and M_0 is denoted by nm_0, where m_0 is the mass of the electron.

For comparison of the two equations and to avoid confusion, suppose that Dirac's equation is multiplied throughout by $(2\pi i/h)\psi^+$, and that the charge e is replaced by $n'e$. If the two equations are then to become identical the factor θ^+ must be replaced by $\psi^+ i\gamma$ and $\gamma\gamma^4$ must be equal to unity.

In Dirac's equation the matrices are constant, the assumption being that there is no gravitational field. Thus in the comparison the matrices of equation (5.18) are also constant and, in particular, γ^4 has the value appropriate to the case when gravitation is neglected. Thus since in this case $\gamma\gamma^4$ must have the value unity the matrix γ must have the constant value acquired by γ^4 when there is no gravitational field.

A comparison of the matrices of the two equations thus gives the following relations when all have the values given by (5.6) and (5.7):

$$a^k = -i\gamma\gamma^k, \quad \beta = -i\gamma\beta. \qquad (5.20)$$

A comparison of the constants gives

$$\frac{\alpha}{l_0} = \frac{e}{hc}, \quad \frac{m_0 c}{h} = \frac{1}{l_0}. \qquad (5.21)$$

To obtain the latter, it should be noted that

$$\frac{i\gamma\gamma_5 n'}{\gamma_{55} l_0} = -M_0 c\beta,$$

and with $\sqrt{(\gamma_{55})}=n'/n$, $M_0=nm_0$, and $i\gamma\gamma_5/\sqrt{(\gamma_{55})}=i\gamma\beta.=-\beta$, the result follows.

Thus $l_0=h/m_0 c$, the length known as the Compton wavelength and $\alpha=e/m_0 c^2$. This value for α was obtained previously (2.54) by the comparison of the equation of the geodesic and the equation of motion of a charged particle in an electromagnetic field, that is to say by comparison of a purely geometrical approach with a purely physical one to the same phenomenon. In this case there was no question of a fundamental length and this could not be expected since its dependence upon Planck's constant reveals it as a characteristic of the quantum theory.

The same geometrical and physical comparisons are now made again. The expression (5.18) is obtained by consideration of geometry and metric, Dirac's equation takes the place in this consideration of the equation of motion of a particle in physics. It is as fundamental as Newton's second law of motion and it can be regarded, like this equation, as a definition of mass, in particular, of the mass, m_0, of an electron.

In the geometrical approach m_0 does not appear. Instead the fundamental length l_0 is introduced, m_0 becomes a symbol for h/cl_0 and arises because the fundamental length exists.

In early attempts to understand the meaning of Schroedinger's function ψ, it was pointed out that it appeared that the length h/m_0c and the proper time h/m_0c^2 were fundamental elements of length and proper time. It was suggested that in considering the motion of a particle of mass m_0, elements of proper time less than h/m_0c^2 had no physical meaning in association with its motion; a law of least time existed.

In the consideration of nuclear field theories the coordinate x^5 does not occur in values less than l_0/n'. It appears like the time t in circuital problems, in which the only importance is that they are periodic and of a certain period. n' is the number of charges associated with a particle of mass nm_0 and it will appear later that the statement that x^5 has no value less than l_0/n' is identical with the statement concerning minimum proper time.

From this point of view the constant m_0 is defined to be h/cl_0 and the concept of mass arises from the existence of a minimum length l_0.

The second term of equation (5.17) can thus be written in the form:

$$\theta^+ \gamma^\mu \frac{\partial \psi}{\partial x^\mu} = \psi^+ \left\{ \left(\frac{\partial}{\partial x^0} + \frac{2\pi i}{h} \frac{n'}{c} \frac{e}{\phi} \right) - \alpha^k \left(\frac{\partial}{\partial x^k} - \frac{2\pi i}{h} \frac{n'}{c} \frac{e}{\phi_k} \right) - \frac{2\pi i}{h} M_0 c\beta \right\} \psi. \quad (5.22)$$

The first term can now be written in the form:

$$\frac{\partial \theta^+}{\partial x^\mu} \gamma^\mu \psi = \left\{ \left(\frac{\partial}{\partial x^0} - \frac{2\pi i}{h} \frac{n' e}{c} \phi \right) \psi^+ \right.$$
$$\left. - \left(\frac{\partial}{\partial x^k} + \frac{2\pi i n' e}{c} \phi_k \right) \psi^+ \alpha^k + \frac{2\pi i M_0 c}{h} \psi^+ \beta \right\} \psi. \quad (5.23)$$

It is evident that these terms are conjugate complex quantities and that they can be written as $\psi^+ i \gamma \gamma^\mu (\partial \psi / \partial x^\mu)$ and $(\partial \psi^+ / \partial x^\mu) i \gamma \gamma^\mu \psi$ respectively. This result has been developed for the case when the matrices (γ^μ) are constants, except for γ^5. But the same is true of these terms when the matrices (γ^μ) have the form given in equation (5.9) as will appear in the last chapter.

For the immediate purpose only the case of constant (γ^m) is required, and in this case the equation (5.16) becomes an identity.

It is convenient to write the equation (5.17) in the form

$$\frac{h}{2\pi i} \psi^+ i \gamma \gamma^\mu \frac{\partial \psi}{\partial x^\mu} + \frac{h}{2\pi i} \frac{\partial \psi^+}{\partial x^\mu} i \gamma \gamma^\mu \psi = \theta^+ R_\mu \gamma^\mu \psi, \quad (5.24)$$

where now the factor $h/2\pi i$ is regarded as absorbed into R_μ. The terms on the left of this equation are now such that the conjugate complex of one is the negative of the other.

If R_μ is placed equal to zero, there being no change in the matrix length as a result of parallel displacement, the condition (5.24) can be satisfied by placing each term on the left of the equation equal to zero, and the result gives Dirac's equation as can be seen from the expressions (5.22) and (5.23). But this is not the only way of satisfying the condition, for if the first term is placed equal to a quantity of the form $\frac{1}{2}(SF^* + S^*F)$, the second will have the value $-\frac{1}{2}(S^*F + SF^*)$ and the condition with $R_\mu = 0$ is still satisfied.

The quantum equation may thus be written as

$$\frac{hc}{2\pi i} \psi^+ i \gamma \gamma^\mu \frac{\partial \psi}{\partial x^\mu} = \frac{1}{2}(SF^* + S^*F), \quad (5.25)$$

where c denotes the velocity of light in empty space, this form being introduced in order to make the expressions on the two sides of the equation representative of energy. It is thus possible to derive Dirac's equation and also a generalization of it from the simple postulate that there shall be no change of matrix length associated with a parallel displacement.

111

Generalizations of Dirac's equation have been introduced in association with nuclear field theories and all are of the type of equation (5.25).

In following Weyl's idea for the electromagnetic theory literally it would appear that R_μ should be a linear function of the field potential components. In a more general expression the field intensities may well be included. From the form of the left-hand side of equation (5.17) it would appear that $\theta^+ R_\mu \gamma^\mu \psi$ would take the form:

$$\theta^+ R_\mu \gamma^\mu \psi = a_1 A^\mu F_\mu + a_2 A^{\mu\nu} F_{\mu\nu} + a_3 A^{\mu\nu\rho} F_{\mu\nu\rho} + \ldots \quad (5.26)$$

where A^μ, $A^{\mu\nu}$, etc., are tensors of the appropriate rank composed of the functions θ^+ and ψ and the matrices (γ^μ). For the vector A^μ the form is

$$A^\mu = \theta^+ \gamma^\mu \psi = \psi^+ i\gamma\gamma^\mu \psi,$$

and for $A^{\mu\nu}$,

$$A^{\mu\nu} = \theta^+ \gamma_5 \gamma^\mu \psi = \psi^+ i\gamma\gamma_5 \gamma^\mu \gamma^\nu \psi$$

and so on.

This seems to be the way to construct these tensors, since the contributions given satisfy the requirements with regard to the rank of the tensor. Thus $A^k = -\psi^+ \alpha^k \psi$ is a well-known vector quantity, while $A^{23} = -\sqrt{(\gamma_{55})}\psi^+ \beta\alpha^2 \alpha^3 \psi$ is a component of a tensor of the second rank. The quantities F_μ, $F_{\mu\nu}$, etc., are ordinary quantities denoting field intensities.

It appears however that for the purpose of obtaining a generalization of the quantum equation appropriate to the field theories introduced in the study of the nucleus, all that is necessary is the introduction of an expression of the form $(SF^* + S^*F)$, leaving the vanishing of $\theta^+ R_\mu \gamma^\mu \psi$ as a general condition to be satisfied in a more general quantum equation. The terms composing this expression will however be constructed in the same way from the field intensity components, θ^+, ψ and (γ^μ).

Suppose that the field is a scalar field, then the term SF^* will take the form $S^\mu F^*_\mu$. If the field is of the vector type the form will be $S^{\mu\nu} F^*_{\mu\nu}$ and so on. All the types of field may exist together and SF^* may thus be the sum of all such terms. It is, however, convenient to consider the terms singly and to write the quantum equation for the scalar field in the form

$$\frac{hc}{2\pi i}\psi^+ i\gamma\gamma^\mu \frac{\partial\psi}{\partial x^\mu} = \tfrac{1}{2}(S^\mu F^*_\mu + S^{*\mu} F_\mu), \quad (5.27)$$

where

$$S^\mu = g_1 \psi^+ i\gamma^\mu \gamma\psi,$$
$$S^{*\mu} = -g_1^* i\psi^+ \gamma\gamma^\mu \psi. \Big\}$$

(5.28)

In the case of the vector field

$$S^{\mu\nu} = g_2 \psi^+ \gamma^\mu \gamma^\nu \gamma_5 \gamma\psi,$$
$$S^{*\mu\nu} = g_2^* \psi^+ \gamma\gamma_5 \gamma^\nu \gamma^\mu \psi, \Big\}$$

(5.29)

of the pseudo-vector field

$$S^{\mu\nu\rho} = g_3 \psi^+ \gamma^\mu \gamma^\nu \gamma^\rho \gamma\psi,$$
$$S^{*\mu\nu\rho} = g_3^* \psi^+ \gamma\gamma^\rho \gamma^\nu \gamma^\mu \psi, \Big\}$$

(5.30)

and of the pseudo-scalar field

$$S^{\mu\nu\rho\sigma} = g_4 \psi^+ \gamma^\mu \gamma^\nu \gamma^\rho \gamma^\sigma \gamma_5 \gamma\psi,$$
$$S^{*\mu\nu\rho\sigma} = g_4^* \psi^+ \gamma\gamma_5 \gamma^\sigma \gamma^\rho \gamma^\nu \gamma^\mu \psi. \Big\}$$

(5.31)

the g's being constant

The operator $K^\mu{}_\lambda$

A form of this operator can be obtained from the identity

$$\frac{\partial \gamma^{\mu\nu}}{\partial x^\sigma} + \Delta^\mu_{\alpha\sigma} \gamma^{\alpha\nu} + \Delta^\nu_{\alpha\sigma} \gamma^{\mu\alpha} = 0.$$

(5.32)

Since $2\gamma^{\mu\nu} = (\gamma^\mu \gamma^\nu + \gamma^\nu \gamma^\mu)$, it follows that this identity can be expressed in the form:

$$K^\mu{}_\sigma \gamma^\nu + \gamma^\mu K^\nu{}_\sigma + K^\nu{}_\sigma \gamma^\mu + \gamma^\nu K^\mu{}_\sigma = 0$$

(5.23)

and this is satisfied identically if $K^\mu{}_\sigma$ is of the form:

$$K^\mu{}_\sigma = \Delta_\sigma \gamma^\mu - \gamma^\mu \Delta_\sigma,$$

(5.34)

where Δ_σ is an undefined operator.

The value of this operator can be determined from the definition of $K^\mu{}_\sigma$ (5.15). This presents no difficulty in the case where there is no gravitational field for in this case the matrices (γ^μ) are constant except for γ^5 which contains the electromagnetic potential (ϕ_m). Thus from

$$\frac{\partial \gamma^\mu}{\partial x^\sigma} + \gamma^\rho \Delta^\mu_{\rho\sigma} = \Delta_\sigma \gamma^\mu - \gamma^\mu \Delta_\sigma,$$

(5.35)

in the case when $\mu = m$, $\sigma = 5$ $(m = 1, 2, 3, 4)$,

$$\gamma^\rho \Delta^m_{\rho 5} = \Delta_5 \gamma^m - \gamma^m \Delta_5.$$

113

From the relation (2.74) this reduces to:

$$\gamma^r \Delta^m_{r5} = \Delta_5 \gamma^m - \gamma^m \Delta_5 \quad (r = 1,2,3,4)$$

and from (2.75)

$$\tfrac{1}{2}\gamma_{55}\,\alpha B_r^{\ m}\gamma^r = \Delta_5\gamma^m - \gamma^m \Delta_5.$$

The suggestion arises from the relation (4.19) that a solution might be obtained by placing $\Delta_5 = F_{\rho\sigma}s^{\rho\sigma}$, with $F_{\rho\sigma}$ antisymmetric in ρ and σ since $s^{\rho\sigma}$ is antisymmetric. Thus the right-hand side becomes

$$F_{\rho\sigma}(s^{\rho\sigma}\gamma^m - \gamma^m s^{\rho\sigma}) = 2F_{\rho\sigma}(\gamma^{\sigma m}\gamma^\rho - \gamma^{\rho m}\gamma^\sigma)$$
$$= 4F_{\rho\sigma}\gamma^{\sigma m}\gamma^\rho$$

and it thus appears that a solution is obtained by placing

$$\gamma^{\sigma m}F_{r\sigma} = \tfrac{1}{8}\gamma_{55}\,\alpha B_r^{\ m}, \quad \gamma^{\sigma m}F_{5\sigma} = 0.$$

By means of the relations (2.61) it may then be shown that

$$\Delta_5 = \tfrac{1}{8}\gamma_{55}\,\alpha B_{mn}s^{mn}, \tag{5.36}$$

summation being for m, $n = 1,2,3,4$, $\neq 5$.

In the same way Δ_n may be found from

$$\frac{\partial \gamma^m}{\partial x^n} + \gamma^\rho \Delta^m_{\rho n} = \Delta_n \gamma^m - \gamma^m \Delta_n.$$

In the absence of a gravitational field the first term on the left-hand side is zero.

$$\gamma^\rho \Delta^m_{\rho n} = \gamma^r \Delta^m_{rn} + \gamma^5 \Delta^m_{5n} = \gamma^r \Delta^m_{rn} + \frac{\gamma_5}{\gamma_{55}}\Delta^m_{5n} - \alpha\phi_l\,\gamma^l \Delta^m_{5n}$$

and on substituting from the relations (2.75) and (2.78) this becomes

$$\gamma^\rho \Delta^m_{\rho n} = \tfrac{1}{2}\gamma_{55}\,\alpha^2\,\phi_n B_r^{\ m}\gamma^r + \tfrac{1}{2}\alpha B_n^{\ m}\gamma_5.$$

Let Δ_n be written as the sum of two parts

$$\Delta_n = \Delta'_n + \Delta''_n.$$

It is then possible to determine Δ'_n from the equation

$$\tfrac{1}{2}\gamma_{55}\,\alpha^2\,\phi_n B_r^{\ m}\gamma^r = \Delta'_n\gamma^m - \gamma^m \Delta'_n$$

and Δ''_n from

$$\tfrac{1}{2}\alpha B_n^{\ m}\gamma_5 = \Delta''_n\gamma^m - \gamma^m \Delta''_n.$$

Thus write $\Delta'_n = \phi_n F_{\rho\sigma} s^{\rho\sigma} = \phi_n F_{rs} s^{rs}$, placing $F_{r5}=0$, $F_{\rho\sigma}$ being assumed to be antisymmetric. Then F_{rs} must be chosen so that

$$\tfrac{1}{2}\gamma_{55}\,\alpha^2\,\phi_n B_r^{\ m}\,\gamma^r = \phi_n F_{rs}(s^{rs}\gamma^m - \gamma^m s^{rs})$$
$$= 2\phi_n F_{rs}(\gamma^{sm}\gamma^r - \gamma^{rm}\gamma^s) = 4\phi_n F_{rs}\gamma^{sm}\gamma^r.$$

Thus

$$\gamma^{sm} F_{rs} = \tfrac{1}{8}\gamma_{55}\,\alpha^2 B_r^{\ m}$$

and, bearing in mind the limitations placed on $(F_{\rho\sigma})$, it follows that

$$F_{rs} = \tfrac{1}{8}\gamma_{55}\,\alpha^2 B_{rs}.$$

Thus

$$\Delta'_n = \tfrac{1}{8}\gamma_{55}\,\alpha^2\,\phi_n B_{rs}s^{rs} \quad (r,s = 1,2,3,4, \neq 5).$$

In order to obtain a value for Δ''_n, write $\Delta''_n = F_{nr}s^r_{\ 5}$. It is therefore required that

$$\tfrac{1}{2}\alpha B_n^{\ m}\gamma_5 = F_{nr}(s^r_{\ 5}\gamma^m - \gamma^m s^r_{\ 5})$$
$$= 2F_{nr}(\gamma^m_{\ 5}\gamma^r - \gamma^{mr}\gamma_5).$$

This follows readily from equations (4.18) and (4.19) and from the relation $s^r_{\ 5} = \gamma_{5\sigma}s^{r\sigma}$.

Since $m \neq 5$, $\gamma^m_{\ 5}=0$ and thus the requirement is

$$\gamma^{mr} F_{nr} = -\tfrac{1}{4}\alpha B_n^{\ m}$$

or

$$F_{nm} = \tfrac{1}{4}\alpha B_{mn},$$

consequently

$$\Delta''_n = \tfrac{1}{4}\alpha B_{rn}s^r_{\ 5}.$$

Thus

$$\Delta_n = \tfrac{1}{4}\alpha B_{rn}s^r_{\ 5} + \tfrac{1}{8}\gamma_{55}\,\alpha^2\,\phi_n B_{rs}s^{rs}. \tag{5.37}$$

On examining the expression

$$K^\mu_{\ \mu} = \Delta_\mu\gamma^\mu - \gamma^\mu\Delta_\mu$$

it is found on substituting the values obtained for the matrices (Δ_μ) that it vanishes identically in agreement with the condition (5.16) which has been regarded as representing a physical law.

Parallel displacement of the gauging factors

The question arises concerning what can be described as a parallel displacement of the factors θ^+ and ψ. The definition of this displacement can be made by considering the vector with components $(\theta^+\gamma^\mu\psi)$.

It can be stated that $\Delta\theta^+$ and $\Delta\psi$ are parallel displacements when, in a change of coordinates by (dx^σ), the vector undergoes a parallel displacement in accordance with the Riemannian definition

$$\Delta(\theta^+ \gamma^\mu \psi) = -\Delta^\mu_{\rho\sigma}(\theta^+ \gamma^\rho \psi)\,dx^\sigma, \qquad (5.38)$$

i.e.

$$\Delta\theta^+ \gamma^\mu \psi + \theta^+ \gamma^\mu \Delta\psi + \theta^+ \frac{\partial\gamma^\mu}{\partial x^\sigma}\psi\,dx^\sigma = -\Delta^\mu_{\rho\sigma}\theta^+ \gamma^\rho \psi\,dx^\sigma$$

or

$$\Delta\theta^+ \gamma^\mu \psi + \theta^+ \gamma^\mu \Delta\psi + \theta^+ (\Delta_\sigma \gamma^\mu - \gamma^\mu \Delta_\sigma - \Delta^\mu_{\rho\sigma}\gamma^\rho)\,\psi\,dx^\sigma$$
$$= -\Delta^\mu_{\rho\sigma}\theta^+ \gamma^\rho \psi\,dx^\sigma.$$

Thus the condition is

$$(\Delta\theta^+ + \theta^+ \Delta_\sigma dx^\sigma)\gamma^\mu \psi + \theta^+ \gamma^\mu(\Delta\psi - \Delta_\sigma \psi\,dx^\sigma) = 0.$$

The appropriate definitions of parallel displacement are therefore

$$\Delta\theta^+ = -\theta^+ \Delta_\sigma dx^\sigma, \quad \Delta\psi = \Delta_\sigma \psi\,dx^\sigma. \qquad (5.39)$$

A note on the character of the additional terms of the generalized quantum equation

The form of these terms is suggested by the discussion on the equation (5.24) and also on the form which the factor R_μ might be expected to take in a more general case. They are to be formed from the matrices and the ψ-factors in such a way that they are the components of vectors and tensors. In constructing these quantities it will be supposed that the gravitational field can be neglected.

In the equation the terms will be multiplied by constant factors such as those of the expression (5.26) where they are denoted by a_1, a_2, etc. These constants will be omitted now since the interest is in the expressions denoted by A^μ, $A^{\mu\nu}$, etc. in (5.26).

The corresponding terms will now be denoted by P^μ, $P^{\mu\nu}$, etc. and from the definition of S^μ in (5.28),

$$P^\mu = \psi^+ i\gamma^\mu \gamma\psi. \qquad (5.40)$$

From the relations (5.1) and (5.20) it follows that

$$P^k = \psi^+ \alpha^k \psi, \quad P_5 = \sqrt{(\gamma_{55})}\,\psi^+ \beta\psi. \qquad (5.41)$$

Thus assuming that α^4 is written for $-i$ the vector (P^k) is a contravariant four-vector and $P_5/\sqrt{(\gamma_{55})}$ a scalar quantity in the four-dimensional continuum.

In agreement with the notation introduced in the relations (2.60) the four-dimensional quantities are

$$p_k = \psi^+ \alpha^k \psi, \quad p_. = \psi^+ \beta \psi. \tag{5.42}$$

The next term in the series contains an antisymmetric tensor of the second rank composed of terms $P^{\mu\nu} (= -P^{\nu\mu})$ defined by

$$P^{\mu\nu} = -\psi^+ \gamma^\mu \gamma^\nu \gamma_5 \gamma\psi, \tag{5.43}$$

the negative sign being introduced for convenience. The term $P^{23} = \sqrt{(\gamma_{55})} \psi^+ i\beta\alpha^2 \alpha^3 \psi$ when multiplied by the factor $he/4\pi m_0 c$ represents a magnetic moment. The term $P^{14} = \sqrt{(\gamma_{55})} \psi^+ \alpha^1 \beta \psi$ when multiplied by $hei/4\pi m_0 c$ represents an electric moment.

Proceeding to a completely antisymmetric tensor of the third rank the definition of a component is:

$$P^{\mu\nu\rho} = \psi^+ \gamma^\mu \gamma^\nu \gamma^\rho \gamma\psi. \tag{5.44}$$

The component

$$P^{234} = \psi^+ \alpha^2 \alpha^3 \psi$$

and

$$P^{123} = -i\psi^+ \alpha^1 \alpha^2 \alpha^3 \psi.$$

When the first of these is multiplied by the factor $hi/4\pi$ it represents a component of angular momentum or spin.

It is interesting to consider the component $P^{23}{}_5$ which is in the four-dimensional continuum a tensor component of the second rank as may be expected from a consideration of the corresponding components of a tensor of the second rank given in the relations (2.41)

$$P^{23}{}_5 = -\sqrt{(\gamma_{55})} \psi^+ i\beta\alpha^2 \alpha^3 \psi$$

and, except for the sign, this is equal to P^{23} considered above. Similarly $P^{14}{}_5$ is equal to P^{14} except for the sign.

Finally the tensor of the fourth rank to be considered is the completely antisymmetric tensor

$$P^{\mu\nu\rho\sigma} = \psi^+ \gamma^\mu \gamma^\nu \gamma^\rho \gamma^\sigma \gamma_5 \gamma\psi. \tag{5.45}$$

The following are typical components:

$$P^{1234} = \sqrt{(\gamma_{55})} \psi^+ \beta\alpha^1 \alpha^2 \alpha^3 \psi, \quad P^{123}{}_5 = -\gamma_{55} \psi^+ i\alpha^1 \alpha^2 \alpha^3 \psi,$$
$$P^{234}{}_5 = \gamma_{55} \psi^+ \alpha^2 \alpha^3 \psi.$$

From the point of view of four dimensions the first of these behaves as a scalar quantity.

Dual quantities

In Chapter 3 it was pointed out that a vector or tensor can be related to another quantity known as its dual by means of a relation such as that illustrated in the expression (3.115). One member of the pair is contravariant and the other covariant in character.

Dual quantities occur in the nuclear field theories which are simple examples of the general case, since they appear when both the gravitational and electromagnetic fields are neglected. In this case the difference between contravariant and covariant quantities can be neglected.

Consider the tensor

$$P'^{\mu\nu} = -\psi^+ \gamma^\mu \gamma^\nu \gamma \psi. \tag{5.46}$$

By means of the relations (5.8) it follows that

and
$$\left.\begin{aligned}
P'^{23} &= \psi^+ \beta\alpha^1 \psi, \\
P'^{14} &= -\psi^+ i\beta\alpha^2 \alpha^3 \psi, \\
P'_5{}^1 &= \sqrt{(\gamma_{55})} \psi^+ \alpha^2 \alpha^3 \psi, \\
P'^4{}_5 &= -\sqrt{(\gamma_{55})} \psi^+ i\alpha^1 \alpha^2 \alpha^3 \psi.
\end{aligned}\right\} \tag{5.47}$$

The components $P^4{}_5{}^1$, $P^{23}{}_5$, P^{234} and P^{123} of the tensor $(P^{\mu\nu\rho})$ have the values:

$$\left.\begin{aligned}
P^4{}_5{}^1 &= \sqrt{(\gamma_{55})} \psi^+ \beta\alpha^1 \psi, \quad P^{23}{}_5 = -\sqrt{(\gamma_{55})} \psi^+ i\beta\alpha^2 \alpha^3 \psi, \\
P^{234} &= \psi^+ \alpha^2 \alpha^3 \psi, \quad P^{123} = -\psi^+ i\alpha^1 \alpha^2 \alpha^3 \psi.
\end{aligned}\right\} \tag{5.48}$$

It thus appears that, except for the factor $\sqrt{(\gamma_{55})}$, these groups of terms have the dual relationship.

If P'^μ be defined as

$$P'^\mu = \psi^+ \gamma^\mu \gamma_5 \gamma \psi, \tag{5.49}$$

$$\left.\begin{aligned}
P'^1 &= \sqrt{(\gamma_{55})} \psi^+ \alpha^2 \alpha^3 \psi, \\
P'^4 &= \sqrt{(\gamma_{55})} \psi^+ i\alpha^1 \alpha^2 \alpha^3 \psi, \\
P'_5 &= \gamma_{55} \psi^+ \beta\alpha^1 \alpha^2 \alpha^3 \psi.
\end{aligned}\right\} \tag{5.50}$$

If these three terms are compared with the components $P^{234}{}_5$, $P_5{}^{123}$ and P^{1234}, it will be found that

$$P^{234}{}_5 = \sqrt{(\gamma_{55})} P'^1, \quad P_5{}^{123} = \sqrt{(\gamma_{55})} P'^4, \quad P^{1234} = \sqrt{(\gamma_{55})} P'_5. \tag{5.51}$$

The importance of these relations is that they have an application in the theory of the nuclear field and that they show the character of the relation which exists between the vector and pseudo-vector fields and the scalar and pseudo-scalar fields respectively.

Bibliography

1. H. T. FLINT, 1935. *Proc. R. Soc.* A, 870, **150**, 421 *sqq.*
2. Y. MIMURA, 1935. *J. Sci. Hiroshima Univ.* A, **5**, 2.
3. Y. MIMURA and H. TAKENO 1962. Reports of Research Institute *Hiroshima University*. No. 2.
4. H. W. HASKEY, 1939. *Phil. Mag.* **7**, XXVII, 221.
5. E. SCHROEDINGER, 1932. *Sber. preuss. Akad. Wiss.*, XI. (For consideration of general relativistic wave equation.)

CHAPTER 6

Continuation of the Field Theories

The scalar field

In the consideration of the different kinds of fields in Chapter 3 the quantities S^μ, $S^{\mu\nu}$, etc., were not defined and the theory was therefore incomplete. But the existence of the expression of the term $(S^*F + SF^*)$ in the quantum equation suggests the idea of an interaction of the field with the particle which the equation represents. It might be said that the S-term is a measure of some property of a particle such as the charge, current, mass or spin. Such terms exist in the equation, viz. $\psi^+ \alpha^k \psi \phi_k$ or $m_0 c \psi^+ \beta \psi$.

The field theory associated with the particle would be expected to contain the same interaction terms. Thus in the scalar field it would be expected that the component S^μ occurring in the Lagrangian is that given in the first of the equations (5.28).

To the Lagrange function must now be added terms so constructed that both the field equations and equation (5.27) can be derived from it.

The appropriate function in the scalar field theory is

$$L = \tfrac{1}{2}(F^{*\mu}F_\mu + g_1^* \psi^+ i\gamma\gamma^\mu \psi F_\mu - g_1 \psi^+ (i\gamma^\mu \gamma\psi F_\mu^*)$$

$$+ \frac{hc}{4\pi i}\left(\psi^+ i\gamma\gamma^\mu \frac{\partial \psi}{\partial x^\mu} - \frac{\partial \psi^+}{\partial x^\mu} i\gamma\gamma^\mu \psi\right), \tag{6.1}$$

where $F_\mu = \partial\theta/\partial x^\mu$. This expression should be compared with that of equation (3.42). L is now a function of $\partial\theta/\partial x^\mu$, $\partial\psi/\partial x^\mu$, ψ and their complex conjugate quantities.

The field equations are derived in the same way as previously in Chapter 3 (3.44).

The quantum equation is

$$\frac{\partial}{\partial x^\mu}\frac{\partial L}{\partial\left(\dfrac{\partial\psi^+}{\partial x^\mu}\right)}-\frac{\partial L}{\partial\psi^+}=0 \qquad (6.2)$$

and this becomes

$$\frac{hc}{2\pi i}i\gamma\gamma^\mu\frac{\partial\psi}{\partial x^\mu}=\tfrac{1}{2}(g_1 i\gamma^\mu\gamma\psi F^*_\mu-g^*_1 i\gamma\gamma^\mu\psi F_\mu)$$

and on multiplying by ψ^+ the equation (5.27) results.

The complex conjugate equation is obtained in a similar way, and is

$$\frac{hc}{2\pi i}\frac{\partial\psi^+}{\partial x^\mu}i\gamma\gamma^\mu=-\tfrac{1}{2}(g_1\psi^+ i\gamma^\mu\gamma F^*_\mu-g^*_1\psi^+ i\gamma\gamma^\mu F_\mu).$$

The energy tensor

In accordance with the definition of this tensor, of which examples have been given in Chapter 3, its value in the present case is:

$$\Theta^\mu_{\ \nu}=\frac{\partial L}{\partial\left(\dfrac{\partial\theta}{\partial x^\mu}\right)}\frac{\partial\theta}{\partial x^\nu}+\frac{\partial L}{\partial\left(\dfrac{\partial\psi}{\partial x^\mu}\right)}\frac{\partial\psi}{\partial x^\nu}+\text{c.c.}-\gamma^\mu_{\ \nu}L. \qquad (6.3)$$

Thus

$$\Theta^\mu_{\ \nu}=\tfrac{1}{2}(V^{*\mu}F_\nu+V^\mu F^*_\nu)+\frac{hc}{4\pi i}\left(\psi^+ i\gamma\gamma^\mu\frac{\partial\psi}{\partial x^\nu}-\frac{\partial\psi^+}{\partial x^\nu}i\gamma\gamma^\mu\psi\right)-\gamma^\mu_{\ \nu}L. \qquad (6.4)$$

The component of this tensor from which the energy density is derived is

$$\Theta^4_{\ 4}=\tfrac{1}{2}(V^{*4}F_4+V^4 F^*_4)+\frac{hc}{4\pi i}\left(\psi^+\frac{\partial\psi}{\partial x^0}-\frac{\partial\psi^+}{\partial x^0}\psi\right)-L. \qquad (6.5)$$

The value of L, on substitution of the terms in the second bracket of the expression (6.1) by means of the quantum equation and its complex conjugate, becomes:

$$L=\tfrac{1}{2}F^{*\mu}F_\mu.$$

121

But $\Theta^4{}_4$ can be also expressed in the form:

$$\Theta^4{}_4 = \tfrac{1}{2}(V^{*4}F_4 + V^4 F^*{}_4) - \tfrac{1}{2}(F^{*\mu}F_\mu - S^{*\mu}F_\mu - S^\mu F^*{}_\mu)$$
$$+ \frac{hc}{4\pi i}\left(\psi^+ \alpha^k \frac{\partial \psi}{\partial x^k} - \frac{\partial \psi^+}{\partial x^k} \alpha^k \psi\right) - n' e\phi_k \psi^+ \alpha^k \psi - n' e\phi\psi^+ \psi$$
$$+ M_0 c^2 \psi^+ \beta\psi, \tag{6.6}$$

which enables the results (3.62) and (3.63) in the earlier consideration of the scalar field to be used. In deriving these results the relation $\operatorname{div} S^k = 0$ was assumed for the static case. Since now $S^k = g_1 \psi^+ \alpha^k \psi$ the condition is appropriate here.

Since

$$s_. = \frac{S_5}{\sqrt{(\gamma_{55})}} = g_1 \psi^+ \beta\psi = s^*_.$$

the value of the energy (3.62) can be expressed in the form:

$$W = -\frac{\kappa^2}{2} \int\int s^*_. s_{.\,a} \phi(r, r_a)\, dv\, dv_a. \tag{6.7}$$

In the case when the field is considered as occupied by isolated particles the integral may be replaced by a double summation by means of the expression (3.63). The constant g_1 is a measure of the strength of the interaction or, in the usual language of field theories, the strength of the source of the field corresponding to charge in the case of a particle generating an electrostatic field.

In the case of a particle with which a function ψ, satisfying Dirac's equation, is associated,

$$\int \psi^+ \beta\psi\, dv = \left(1 - \frac{v^2}{c^2}\right)^{1/2}$$

in the case of plane waves in the absence of a field. The quantity v represents the velocity of the particle and in the static case ($v = 0$), the integral has the value unity and $\psi^+ \beta\psi$ may be replaced by $\psi_a^+ \psi_a$. Thus if a particle occupies a point a, the integral (6.7) becomes

$$W = -\frac{\kappa^2}{2} \int\int g_1^* g_1 \psi^+ \psi\psi^+{}_a \psi_a \phi(r, r_a)\, dv\, dv_a. \tag{6.8}$$

If the expression $\psi^+ \psi g_1 dv$ is replaced by $\bar{g}_1$ and this expression is applied to a collection of individual particles of small extent, the energy becomes

$$W = -\frac{\kappa^2}{2} \sum_a \bar{g}_1 \bar{g}_1 \phi(r_b, r_a). \tag{6.9}$$

The quantity $\bar{g}_1$ may be regarded as the strength of the source. In the integration, or summation, ϕ becomes infinite when $r_a = r_b$, but if the idea that two particles can approach infinitely close together is not a physical one, it may be possible to avoid the infinity in the case when $r_a = r_b$. This would agree with a suggestion that every mass is associated with extent so that the particle of large-scale physics, which is regarded as a point, is an approximation which is not valid in the small-scale world.

The additional terms on the right-hand side of equation (5.27), taken to the approximation considered in connection with the energy (6.6), become $\frac{1}{2}(S^{*5}F_5 + S^5 F^*_5)$ and on the assumption that $S_5 = \sqrt{(\gamma_{55})}g_1\psi^+\beta\psi$ the additional amount is $(n'/n)g_1\psi^+\beta\psi F_5$.

Thus the quantum equation now contains two terms in $\psi^+\beta\psi$, viz.

$$\left(M_0 c^2 - \frac{n'}{n}g_1 F_5\right)\psi^+\beta\psi. \tag{6.10}$$

If Dirac's equation is regarded as defining the rest mass of the particle considered, it appears that in this case the rest mass

$$M'_0 = M_0 - \frac{n' g_1 F_5}{nc^2}. \tag{6.11}$$

M_0 occurs from the acceptance of the existence of a fundamental length l_0 and the additional term arises from interaction with the field.

The vector field

From the more general form of the quantum equation it appears that in the case of a particle associated with the vector field it should become

$$\frac{hc}{2\pi i}\psi^+ i\gamma\gamma^\mu \frac{\partial\psi}{\partial x^\mu} = \frac{1}{4}(S^{\mu\nu}F^*_{\mu\nu} + S^{*\mu\nu}F_{\mu\nu}). \tag{6.12}$$

The factor $\frac{1}{4}$ is introduced in order to keep down the number of terms, for example in the case of $\mu = 2,3$, $\nu = 3,2$, $S^{23}F^*_{23} = S^{32}F^*_{32}$.

The Lagrange density function in this case is

$$L = \frac{1}{4}(F^{*\mu\nu}F_{\mu\nu} - S^{*\mu\nu}F_{\mu\nu} - S^{\mu\nu}F^*_{\mu\nu})$$
$$+ \frac{hc}{4\pi i}\left(\psi^+ i\gamma\gamma^\mu \frac{\partial\psi}{\partial x^\mu} - \frac{\partial\psi^+}{\partial x^\mu} i\gamma\gamma^\mu \psi\right), \tag{6.13}$$

123

with
$$S^{\mu\nu} = g_2 \psi^+ \gamma^\mu \gamma^\nu \gamma_5 \gamma\psi, \quad S^{*\mu\nu} = g_2^* \psi^+ \gamma\gamma_5 \gamma^\nu \gamma^\mu \psi. \quad (6.14)$$

It is clear from the treatment of the vector field in Chapter 3 and from the method of Lagrange applied to the expression (6.13) that the field equations and the quantum equation together with its conjugate equation can be derived in the usual way.

The energy tensor, derived in accordance with the method explained in Chapter 4 is:

$$T^\mu_{\ \nu} = \tfrac{1}{2}(V^{*\mu\alpha}F_{\nu\alpha} + V^{\mu\alpha}F^*_{\nu\alpha})$$
$$+ \frac{hc}{4\pi i}\left(\psi^+ i\gamma\gamma^\mu \frac{\partial\psi}{\partial x^\nu} - \frac{\partial\psi^+}{\partial x^\nu} i\gamma\gamma^\mu \psi\right) - \gamma^\mu_{\ \nu}L. \quad (6.15)$$

In this expression the field components occur in the symmetric form but the terms in ψ are not symmetrical and are left for convenience in the form in which they occur.

The energy density is thus given by

$$-T^4_{\ 4} = -\tfrac{1}{2}(V^{*4\alpha}F_{4\alpha} + V^{4\alpha}F^*_{4\alpha}) - \frac{hc}{4\pi i}\left(\psi^+ \frac{\partial\psi}{\partial x^0} - \frac{\partial\psi^+}{\partial x^0}\psi\right) + L \quad (6.16)$$

or, since according to (6.12) and (6.13) $L = \tfrac{1}{4}F^{*\mu\nu}F_{\mu\nu}$,

$$-T^4_{\ 4} = -\tfrac{1}{2}(V^{*4\alpha}F_{4\alpha} + V^{4\alpha}F^*_{4\alpha}) + \tfrac{1}{4}(F^{*\mu\nu}F_{\mu\nu} - S^{*\mu\nu}F_{\mu\nu} - S^{\mu\nu}F^*_{\mu\nu})$$
$$+ \frac{hc}{4\pi i}\left(\frac{\partial\psi^+}{\partial x^k}\alpha^k\psi - \psi^+ \alpha^k \frac{\partial\psi}{\partial x^k}\right)$$
$$+ e\phi_k\psi^+ \alpha^k\psi + e\phi\psi^+\psi - M_0 c^2 \psi^+ \beta\psi \quad (6.17)$$

assuming $n' = 1$.

The right-hand side may be described as field and interaction energy and particle energy, the latter consisting of the terms in ψ.

The field and interaction terms are the same as those considered in Chapter 3 (cf. equation 3.71) and with the same restrictions lead to the energy value given by the sum of the expressions (3.98) and (3.103) or by (3.104).

The values of the quantities denoted by ρ and I in these expressions are required in terms of ψ and ψ^+ and the matrices.

From the values given in the relations (3.88) it appears that

$\rho = -(k/\gamma_{55})S_5{}^4$ and thus according to the definitions (6.14), since $\gamma_5\gamma_5 = \gamma_{55}$,

$$\rho = kg_2\psi^+\psi. \qquad (6.18)$$

From the values given in the table (3.83)

$$I_x = S^{23} = g_2\psi^+\gamma^2\gamma^3\gamma_5\gamma\psi = -g_2\sqrt{(\gamma_{55})}\,\psi^+i\beta\alpha^2\alpha^3\psi. \qquad (6.19)$$

It should be noted that from the four-dimensional point of view the components of $\mathbf{I}$, and of the polarization P, form a tensor of the second rank, while those of the density ρ, and of the current $\mathbf{J}$, form a four-vector. Thus it is not necessary to suppose that the constant multiplier g_2, should be the same in the two groups of terms. The requirements of covariance are fulfilled if the multiplier in (6.18) differs from that of (6.19). It is convenient to write these quantities so that, apart from the constants, they are in the self-conjugate form, e.g. $\psi^+i\beta\alpha^2\alpha^3\psi$ and $\psi^+\psi$. Thus the density will be expressed by

$$\left.\begin{aligned}\rho &= kg_2'\psi^+\psi \\[4pt] I_x &= \sqrt{(\gamma_{55})}\,g_2\psi^+i\beta\alpha^2\alpha^3\psi.\end{aligned}\right\} \qquad (6.20)$$

and the moment

The values of q and m_x in the formula (3.104) are

$$kg_2'\psi^+\psi\,dv \quad \text{and} \quad \sqrt{(\gamma_{55})}\,g_2\psi^+i\beta\alpha^2\alpha^3\psi\,dv.$$

Assuming that the field contains small isolated particles these quantities are denoted by

$$q = k\bar{g}_2'\psi^+\psi \quad \text{and} \quad I_x = \sqrt{(\gamma_{55})}\,\bar{g}_2\psi^+i\beta\alpha^2\alpha^3\psi, \qquad (6.21)$$

with similar expressions for I_y and I_z.

It will be noted that k is the universal constant $2\pi m_0c/\hbar$, m_0 denoting the mass of an electron while $\sqrt{(\gamma_{55})} = n'/n$, n' being the number of fundamental charges present and n the number of fundamental masses.

From the point of view now proposed the quantities consisting of ψ, ψ^+ and the matrices are geometrical in the same sense that the components (g_{mn}) are geometrical in the theory of relativity. They are not essentially measures of properties of particles. The particle aspect is represented by $\sqrt{(\gamma_{55})}$, g_2' and g_2.

The pseudo-vector field

In this case, as has already appeared in Chapter 3, the field components are completely antisymmetrical tensors of the third rank. The Lagrange density takes the form:

$$L = \frac{1}{4}\frac{1}{3!}\,(V^{*\lambda\mu\nu}\,V_{\lambda\mu\nu} + V^{*}_{\lambda\mu\nu}S^{\lambda\mu\nu} + V_{\lambda\mu\nu}S^{*\lambda\mu\nu})$$

$$+ \frac{hc}{4\pi i}\left(\psi^{+}i\gamma\gamma^{\mu}\frac{\partial\psi}{\partial x^{\mu}} - \frac{\partial\psi^{+}}{\partial x^{\mu}}i\gamma\gamma^{\mu}\psi\right) \tag{6.22}$$

$$= \tfrac{1}{4}(V^{*\alpha\beta}\,V_{\alpha\beta} + V^{*}_{\alpha\beta}S^{\alpha\beta} + V_{\alpha\beta}S^{*\alpha\beta})$$

$$+ \frac{hc}{4\pi i}\left(\psi^{+}i\gamma\gamma^{\mu}\frac{\partial\psi}{\partial x^{\mu}} - \frac{\partial\psi^{+}}{\partial x^{\mu}}i\gamma\gamma^{\mu}\psi\right), \tag{6.23}$$

where for convenience the same letters are used for the tensors and their duals.

The quantum equations in this case are:

$$\frac{hc}{2\pi i}\psi^{+}i\gamma\gamma^{\mu}\frac{\partial\psi}{\partial x^{\mu}} = \tfrac{1}{4}(V^{*}_{\alpha\beta}S^{\alpha\beta} + V_{\alpha\beta}S^{*\alpha\beta}), \tag{6.24}$$

and the conjugate equation

$$\frac{hc}{2\pi i}\frac{\partial\psi^{+}}{\partial x^{\mu}}i\gamma\gamma^{\mu}\psi = -\tfrac{1}{4}(V_{\alpha\beta}S^{*\alpha\beta} + V^{*}_{\alpha\beta}S^{\alpha\beta}) \tag{6.25}$$

with

$$\left.\begin{aligned}S^{\mu\nu\rho} &= g_3\,\psi^{+}\,\gamma^{\mu}\,\gamma^{\nu}\,\gamma^{\rho}\,\gamma\psi,\\ S^{\mu\nu} &= -g_3\,\psi^{+}\,\gamma^{\mu}\,\gamma^{\nu}\,\gamma\psi.\end{aligned}\right\} \tag{6.26}$$

With these values the formula (3.150) is applicable, the values of P and J being derived from the relations (3.132) and (3.133).

The pseudo-scalar field

By continuing in accordance with the preceding cases it appears that for the pseudo-scalar field the Lagrange density function is:

$$L = \frac{1}{2}\frac{1}{4!}\,(V^{*\lambda\mu\nu\rho}\,V_{\lambda\mu\nu\rho} + V^{*}_{\lambda\mu\nu\rho}S^{\lambda\mu\nu\rho} + V_{\lambda\mu\nu\rho}S^{*\lambda\mu\nu\rho})$$

$$+ \frac{hc}{4\pi i}\left(\psi^{+}i\gamma\gamma^{\mu}\frac{\partial\psi}{\partial x^{\mu}} - \frac{\partial\psi^{+}}{\partial x^{\mu}}i\gamma\gamma^{\mu}\psi\right) \tag{6.27}$$

$$= \tfrac{1}{2}(V^{*}_{\mu}\,V^{\mu} + V^{*}_{\mu}S^{\mu} + V_{\mu}S^{*\mu})$$

$$+ \frac{hc}{4\pi i}\left(\psi^{+}i\gamma\gamma^{\mu}\frac{\partial\psi}{\partial x^{\mu}} - \frac{\partial\psi^{+}}{\partial x^{\mu}}i\gamma\gamma^{\mu}\psi\right),$$

with

$$S^{\lambda\mu\nu\rho} = g_4 \psi^+ \gamma^\lambda \gamma^\mu \gamma^\nu \gamma^\rho \gamma_5 \gamma \psi, \qquad (6.28)$$

$$S^\mu = g_4 \psi^+ \gamma^\mu \gamma_5 \gamma \psi.$$

The formula (3.166) is applicable in this case, the values of the components of S^k and S^{*k} being obtained from the expression in (6.28), for example,

$$S^1 = g_4 \sqrt{(\gamma_{55})} \psi^+ \alpha^2 \alpha^3 \psi, \quad S^4 = -\sqrt{(\gamma_{55})} g_4 \psi^+ i\alpha^1 \alpha^2 \alpha^3 \psi,$$

$$S_5 = \gamma_{55} g_4 \psi^+ \beta \alpha^1 \alpha^2 \alpha^3 \psi.$$

The theory of the electron

In the theory of the electron it is assumed that its own field is of a vector character, the potential being (U_m), of which the fifth component U_5 is zero. The field components (F_{mn}) are derived from U_m by means of the relations:

$$F_{mn} = \frac{\partial U_n}{\partial x^m} - \frac{\partial U_m}{\partial x^n}. \qquad (6.29)$$

A second field tensor (V^{mn}) is introduced as in Chapter 3, and in agreement with the relations (3.79) sqq., it is convenient to write:

$$\left. \begin{array}{l} F_{23} = B_x, \text{ etc.}, \ F_{41} = iE_x, \text{ etc.}, \\ V^{23} = H_x, \text{ etc.}, \ V^{41} = iD_x, \text{ etc.}, \\ S^{23} = I_x, \text{ etc.}, \ S^{41} = -iP_x, \text{etc.}, \ S_5{}^k = \dfrac{i\gamma_{55}}{k} J^k, \ S_5{}^4 = \dfrac{-\gamma_{55}}{k} \rho \\ \text{with} \\ B_x = H_x + I_x, \ D_x = E_x + P_x, \text{ etc.} \end{array} \right\} (6.30)$$

A distinction between the vector (U_m) and the vector (ϕ_m) must be borne in mind, the latter refers to the external field, the former to the electron field. Moreover it is assumed that the components (U_m) depend on the fifth coordinate in the usual way, viz.

$$\frac{\partial U_m}{\partial x^5} = \frac{2\pi i n'}{l_0} U_m,$$

n' denoting the number of charges associated with the particle. In the present case $n' = -1$. The number n in this case is unity. The case now to be considered is that of an electron located in a region in which no field exists except its own field.

The quantum equation thus becomes:

$$\frac{hc}{2\pi i}\psi^+ \frac{\partial \psi}{\partial x^0} = \frac{hc}{2\pi i}\psi^+ \alpha^k \frac{\partial \psi}{\partial x^k} + m_0 c^2 \psi^+ \beta\psi + \tfrac{1}{4}(S^{\mu\nu}F^*_{\mu\nu} + S^{*\mu\nu}F_{\mu\nu})$$

(6.31)

and $S^{\mu\nu}$ has the value appropriate to the vector field, viz.

$$S^{\mu\nu} = g_2\psi^+ \gamma^\mu \gamma^\nu \gamma_5 \gamma\psi.$$

It thus appears that $S^{23} = -g_2\psi^+ i\alpha^2 \alpha^3 \beta\psi$ and if $\mu_0 = he/4\pi m_0 c$ this can be expressed in terms of the fundamental magnetic moment by writing $a_2 = -g_2/\mu_0$ as

$$S^{23} = a_2\mu_0 \psi^+ i\alpha^2 \alpha^3 \beta\psi.$$

(6.32)

Similarly it is found that

$$S^{41} = -ia_2\sqrt{(\gamma_{55})}\mu_0 \psi^+ i\alpha^1 \beta\psi$$

and $\mu_0\psi^+ i\alpha^1 \beta\psi$ is a component of the fundamental electric moment.

From the relations (6.30) it thus follows that

$$I_x = a_2\mu_0\psi^+ i\alpha^2 \alpha^3 \beta\psi, \quad P_x = n' a_2\mu_0\psi^+ i\alpha^1 \beta\psi.$$

(6.33)

The components with the suffix 5, viz. $S^k{}_5$ and $S^4{}_5$ have the values:

$$S^k{}_5 = -i\gamma_{55}g_2\psi^+ \alpha^k \psi \quad \text{and} \quad S^4{}_5 = g_2\gamma_{55}\psi^+ \psi.$$

Thus from (6.30)

$$J^k = g_2 k\psi^+ \alpha^k \psi, \quad \rho = g_2 k\psi^+ \psi.$$

(6.34)

Since (J^k, ρ) forms a four-vector and (S^{mn}) is a tensor, four-dimensional covariance is preserved if the constant g_2 in the relations (6.34) is not equal to that associated with such terms as S^{23} and S^{41}. Thus a constant a'_2 independent of a_2 can be associated with J^k and ρ and by writing $a'_2 = 2\pi g_2/l_0$ these terms become:

$$J^k = a'_2 n' \psi^+ \alpha^k \psi, \quad \rho = a'_2 n' \psi^+ \psi.$$

(6.35)

If all quantities I, B, etc., are real, except for the exponential factor in x^5, and since the products $S^{\mu\nu}$ and $F_{\mu\nu}$ do not contain x^5, the additional terms may be written in the form:

$$(I.B + P.E + J.U + \rho U_0), \quad \text{with } U_4 = -iU_0,$$

(6.36)

where x^5 does not now occur. All the terms of this expression do not appear to be necessary in considering the theory of the electron and for simplicity the last two are considered.

If Dirac's equation is considered as the equation which defines the mass, m_0', of the particle, then according to equation (6.31) and the expression (6.36)

$$m_0' c^2 \psi^+ \beta\psi = m_0 c^2 \psi^+ \beta\psi + J \cdot U + \rho U_0 \qquad (6.37)$$

or

$$m_0' c^2 \psi^+ \beta\psi = m_0 c^2 \psi^+ \beta\psi + a_2' n'(\psi^+ a^k \psi U_k + \psi^+ \psi U_0). \qquad (6.38)$$

There is thus an additional mass due to the field of the particle given by

$$(m_0' - m_0) \psi^+ \beta\psi = \frac{a_2'}{c^2} n' \psi^+ (\alpha^k U_k + U_0) \psi. \qquad (6.39)$$

The expression $m_0'\beta$ in the quantum theory is equivalent to $m' = m_0'/\sqrt{[1(-v^2/c^2)]}$, so that in the static case the expression $\psi^+ \beta\psi$ can be replaced by $\psi^+ \psi$ and on integrating throughout space

$$m_0' - m_0 = \frac{a_2' n'}{c^2} \int \psi^+ (\alpha^k U_k + U_0) \psi dv. \qquad (6.40)$$

In the theory given here there is nothing to indicate the value of a_2' but some writers give it the value e where e is the fundamental unit of electric charge, i.e. the charge of the positron.

In the consideration of the self-energy of an electron in the classical theory the amount accounted for is that denoted by $m_0 c^2$. In the quantum theory there is additional amount described as interaction energy which is denoted by the integral term of the expression (6.40) [2].

It is again interesting to note that in the present theory the quantity $m_0 c^2$ arises from the assumption that a fundamental length, l_0, exists, while the second, which comes into consideration with the derivation of the quantum equation, may from its form be described as due to interaction energy.

The difficulty associated with the integral is that the calculations lead to an infinite value, and, to avoid it, it is necessary to assume arbitrarily a finite limit to the integration over certain frequencies associated with the Fourier expansion of the vector potential.

The value of this addition to the rest mass depends on the quantum state of the particle, that is to say, upon the value of ψ which occurs in the expressions for the current density **J** and for the charge density ρ. It is of interest to note that in his explanation of the phenomenon of the Lamb–Retherford shift, H. A. Bethe concludes, 'that the level shift due to interaction with radiation is a real effect and is of finite magnitude' [3].

Current density

In Kaluza's theory the component $T^m{}_5$ of the energy tensor represents the current density after multiplication by a suitable constant (cf. equation 2.94).

The vanishing of the divergence of the tensor gives for the case $\nu = 5$,

$$\frac{\partial T^m{}_5}{\partial x^m} = 0,$$

since $\partial T^5{}_5 / \partial x^5$ vanishes.

The structure of the tensor $(T^\mu{}_\nu)$ makes it clear that it is independent of x^5, the various terms being products of two quantities one of which contains e^{ikx^5} and the other e^{-ikx^5}. This equation thus expresses the conservation of charge.

In the case of the vector field (equation 6.15),

$$T^m{}_5 = \tfrac{1}{2}(V^{*mn}F_{5n} + V^{mn}F^*_{5n}) + \frac{hn'c}{l_0}\psi^+ i\gamma\gamma^m\psi \qquad (6.41)$$

$$-\alpha T^m{}_5 = -\tfrac{1}{2}\alpha(V^{*mn}F_{5n} + V^{mn}F^*_{5n}) + n'e\psi^+\alpha^m\psi, \qquad (6.42)$$

where α is the constant $e/m_0 c^2$.

In the case $m = 4$, $\alpha^4 = -i$ and it thus appears that the last term of the expression (6.42) represents the current density of the particle for the case when $k = 1, 2, 3$ and, in the case when $m = 4$, it denotes $i\rho$ where ρ is the charge density.

This theory indicates that there is an addition to this particle current arising from the field in the same way that there is additional energy existing in the field.

The angular momentum tensor

The simplest application of the angular momentum tensor occurs in the case of a particle in the absence of a nuclear field. The Lagrange density function is then

$$L = \frac{hc}{4\pi i}\left(\psi^+ i\gamma\gamma^\mu \frac{\partial\psi}{\partial x^\mu} - \frac{\partial\psi^+}{\partial x^\mu} i\gamma\gamma^\mu\psi\right) \qquad (6.43)$$

and the energy tensor

$$\Theta^\mu{}_\nu = \frac{hc}{4\pi i}\left(\psi^+ i\gamma\gamma^\mu \frac{\partial\psi}{\partial x^\nu} - \frac{\partial\psi^+}{\partial x^\nu} i\gamma\gamma^\mu \psi\right) - \delta^\mu{}_\nu L \qquad (6.44)$$

and from the equation (4.22)

$$H^{\mu\lambda\rho} = \frac{hc}{16\pi i}\{\psi^+ i\gamma(\gamma^\mu s^{\lambda\rho} - s^{\rho\lambda}\gamma^\mu)\,\psi\} \qquad (6.45)$$

and according to the expression (4.28) a component of the angular momentum tensor is given by

$$M^{\mu\lambda\rho} = x^\lambda \Theta^{\mu\rho} - x^\rho \Theta^{\mu\lambda} + H^{\mu\lambda\rho} - H^{\mu\rho\lambda}. \qquad (6.46)$$

A component of angular momentum is

$$M^{4\lambda\rho} = x^\lambda \Theta^{4\rho} - x^\rho \Theta^{4\lambda} + H^{4\lambda\rho} - H^{4\rho\lambda}. \qquad (6.47)$$

But when the matrices are constant as is now supposed, it readily follows that

$$H^{4\lambda\rho} - H^{4\rho\lambda} = \frac{hc}{4\pi}\psi^+ s^{\lambda\rho}\psi. \qquad (6.48)$$

By comparison with the tensor component of the expression (2.87), from which it appears that $T^{4k} = ic\rho(dx^k/dt)$, where $\rho = \rho_0[(dt/d\tau)]^2$, it follows that the angular moment density is obtained from $M^{4\lambda\rho}/ic$.

Thus the last two terms of the expression (6.47) add $(h/4\pi i)\psi^+ s^{\lambda\rho}\psi$ to the orbital momentum to make up the total angular momentum. This term is the spin angular momentum density.

The localization or coordinate operator

In the discussion of Kaluza's theory in the first chapter it appeared that the new components of the energy tensor, resulting from the introduction of a fifth coordinate, brought the current density into close association with the energy and momentum densities, making energy, momentum and current parts of a single quantity. It is thus suggested that the additional components of the angular momentum be examined and their meaning interpreted.

From the expression (6.47) the value of the component $M^{4\lambda}{}_5$ is given by

$$M^{4\lambda}{}_5 = x^\lambda \Theta^4{}_5 - x_5 \Theta^{4\lambda} + \frac{hc}{4\pi}\psi^+ s^\lambda{}_5 \psi, \qquad (6.49)$$

after making use of the expression (6.48).

From the expression (6.44) it follows that

$$\Theta^4{}_5 = m_0 c^2 n' i\psi^+ \psi, \tag{6.50}$$

$$\Theta^{4\lambda} = \frac{ic}{2} \gamma^{\lambda\rho} \left(\psi^+ \frac{h}{2\pi i} \frac{\partial \psi}{\partial x^\rho} - \frac{h}{2\pi i} \frac{\partial \psi^+}{\partial x^\rho} \psi \right).$$

If the operator

$$p_\rho = \frac{h}{2\pi i} \frac{\partial}{\partial x^\rho},$$

this can be written

$$\Theta^{4\lambda} = \frac{ic}{2} \gamma^{\lambda\rho} (\psi^+ p_\rho \psi + \psi^+ p_\rho^* \psi)$$

so that writing $P_\rho = \frac{1}{2}(p_\rho + p_\rho^*)$, the momentum is given by $\psi^+ P_\rho \psi$ and

$$\Theta^{4\lambda} = ic\psi^+ P^\lambda \psi \tag{6.51}$$

and if p_ρ is *real*, $P_\rho = p_\rho = p_\rho^*$.

In the case in which $\lambda = k$ $(1, 2, 3)$,

$$M^{4k}{}_5 = m_0 c^2 in' x^k \psi^+ \psi - icx_5 \psi^+ P^k \psi + \frac{hc}{4\pi} \psi^+ s^k{}_5 \psi$$

or

$$\frac{M^{4k}{}_5}{m_0 c^2 i} = \psi^+ \left(n' x^k - \frac{x_5}{m_0 c} P^k + \frac{h}{4\pi m^0 c} \frac{n'}{n} i\beta\alpha^k \right) \psi. \tag{6.52}$$

The expression within the brackets is

$$n' \left(x^k - \frac{x_5}{n' m_0 c} P^k + \frac{h}{4\pi n m_0 c} i\beta\alpha^k \right)$$

and the suggestion arises that the operator

$$X^k = x^k - \frac{x_5}{n' m_0 c} P^k + \frac{h}{4\pi n m_0 c} i\beta\alpha^k \tag{6.53}$$

should be regarded as a coordinate or localization operator.

The fourth component is

$$X^4 = x^4 - \frac{x_5}{n' m_0 c} P^4 + \frac{h}{4\pi n m_0 c} \beta. \tag{6.54}$$

The forms of these operators suggest that the simple localization of a particle by the coordinates (x^1, x^2, x^3) or (x, y, z) is incomplete; its momentum must also be taken into account and, in addition, there is a third intrinsic quantity containing the matrices. The structure of this operator is similar to that of the angular momentum operator consisting of two terms representing the orbital angular momentum and a third representing the intrinsic angular momentum or spin.

In the case of the electron the spin has the values $\pm h/4\pi$ and in the case of the coordinate operator the intrinsic part has the values $\pm h/4\pi M_0 c$.

If the case of a particle at rest be considered the operator becomes

$$\left(x^\lambda + \frac{h}{4\pi M_0 c} i\beta\alpha^\lambda\right)$$

and this may be interpreted by stating that, if a particle has the coordinates (x^1, x^2, x^3) in the usual sense, in a quantum mechanical description there is a departure from the idea that it is exactly located at this point.

It is interesting to examine the quantity

$$R = \psi^+ \alpha_m X^m \psi. \tag{6.55}$$

This quantity is a matrix operator similar to that defined in the equation (5.11), there being in this case no component X^5, since this vanishes on account of the antisymmetry of $M^{4\lambda\mu}$.

On substituting for the value of X^m the term $\psi^+ \alpha_m P^m \psi$ appears in R. But from the simple form of Dirac's equation which appears in this consideration where no interaction terms are included (cf. 6.31) it follows that this term is equal to $-nm_0 c\psi^+ \beta\psi$. Thus

$$R = \psi^+ \left(\alpha_m x^m + \frac{n}{n'} x_5 \beta - \frac{hi}{\pi m_0 c} \beta\right)\psi \tag{6.56}$$

and the last term of this expression is imaginary.

The real part of the expression is

$$\operatorname{Re} R = \psi^+ \left(\alpha_m x^m + \frac{x_5}{\surd(\gamma_{55})} \beta\right)\psi. \tag{6.57}$$

The characteristic values of this expression are

$$\pm \left(\Sigma (x^m)^2 + \frac{x_5{}^2}{\gamma_{55}}\right).$$

This agrees with the expression (2.46) for the line element.

The introduction of the co-ordinate operators thus agrees with the suggestion that the geometrical basis of the world of small-scale phenomena is the introduction of a metric defined by

$$d\sigma = \gamma_\mu dx^\mu.$$

Concept of a minimum length

In association with the early attempts at an explanation of the significance of Schroedinger's equation and of the meaning of the function ψ it was pointed out that the quantum theory seemed to imply the existence of a minimum proper length- and time-interval.[4] The statement was made that, in considering the motion of a fundamental particle, no physical significance could be given to an interval of proper length less than $h/M_0 c$ or of proper time less than $h/M_0 c^2$, M_0 being the rest mass of the particle. The statement implies the existence of a principle of least time, and, since the time of the original suggestions, other arguments have been advanced leading to the same conclusion.

Other writers have suggested from different points of view and in different associations that a minimum length $e^2/m_0 c^2$ exists, m_0 being the mass of the electron, and suggestions of the existence of a 'cut-off' in nuclear physics, in so far as the cut-off is a length or time, is possibly associated with the same phenomenon.

One of the outstanding exponents of this view was Arthur March, who proposed a system of geometry based on the concept of the existence of a minimum length, space having the character of a cell-like structure. He believed that with the acceptance of this concept difficulties concerning the existence of infinite magnitudes in quantum electrodynamics and nuclear field theories could be avoided [5].

The original form of the principle of least time can be introduced very simply in the notation of this work, where it becomes the statement that the coordinate x^5 can only undergo changes of integral multiples of the fundamental length l_0/n' when it is used as a co-ordinate of a particle carrying a charge $n'e$, e denoting the charge of a positron.

In accordance with one of the equations (2.60), writing $A^5 = dx^5$,

$$dx^5 = \frac{dx_5}{\gamma_{55}} - \alpha\phi_m dx^m. \tag{6.58}$$

134

Thus if $dx^5 \nless l_0/n'$, since $dx_5 = \sqrt{(\gamma_{55})}\,c\,d\tau$ and $\sqrt{(\gamma_{55})} = n'/n$,

$$d\tau \nless \frac{l_0}{nc} + \frac{n'\alpha}{nc}\,\phi_m\,dx^m.$$

This represents a more general statement than the original one which applied to a free particle and was equivalent to $d\tau \nless l_0/nc$ and since $l_0 = h/m_0 c$, writing $nm_0 = M_0$, the rest mass of the particle, it follows that $d\tau \nless h/M_0 c^2$.

Bibliography

1. L. DE BROGLIE, 1945. *De la Mécanique ondulatoire à la Théorie du Noyau*, Chap. XV. Hermann et Cie.
2. V. S. WEISSKOPF, 1939. *Phys. Rev.*, **56**, 72.
3. H. A. BETHE, 1947. *Phys. Rev.*, **72**, 339.
4. H. T. FLINT, 1927. *Proc. R. Soc.* A, **117**, 630.
5. A. MARCH, 1951. *Quantum Mechanics of Particles and Wave Fields*, Chap. X. John Wiley and Sons.

CHAPTER 7

The Basis of the Theory in Accordance with the Principles and Notation of the General Theory of Relativity

Progress can be made in the attempt to express the principles of the quantum theory in the notation of the general theory of relativity by a suggestion taken from Einstein's theory of distant parallelism [1], [2]. This was contained in a system of geometry used by him in an attempt to discover a unified field theory of gravitation and electromagnetism.

Although Einstein introduced vectors with five components in his notation he retained the four-dimensional continuum as a fundamental background and related the vectors with five components to four-dimensional vectors.

In the present theory four-dimensional invariance is retained but the view taken is that, in order to make an appeal to the forms of geometry in describing phenomena of the macroscopic and microscopic worlds or rather of the world of which these regions are parts, a continuum of at least five dimensions is necessary. Thus the system of Einstein's theory of distant parallelism is interpreted to suit the present purpose in the following way.

At any point of space, and for a small region round it, it is possible to set up two systems of axes which may be used as axes of reference for localization. The sets each consist of five coordinate axes, one set can be described as natural or curvilinear axes and will be denoted by unit vectors (ϵ_μ) and the other can be described as rectilinear axes denoted by (i_α).

Any vector, A, existing in the neighbourhood of the point in question may be represented by:

$$\left.\begin{array}{l} A = X^{\mu}\,\epsilon_{\mu} \\[2mm] A = Z_{\alpha}\,i_{\alpha}. \end{array}\right\} \tag{7.1}$$

or

In this formalism X^{μ} is the contravariant component of the vector A but it will be assumed to be possible to make use of the alternative representations

$$A = X_{\mu}\,\epsilon^{\mu} \tag{7.2}$$

where X_{μ} is the covariant component of A.

The axes (ϵ^{μ}) are regarded as appropriate curvilinear axes when representation in terms of covariant components is required.

The rectilinear axes possess the property of orthogonality

$$i_{\alpha}.i_{\beta} = \delta_{\alpha\beta} \tag{7.3}$$

and the curvilinear axes satisfy the following relations:

$$\left.\begin{array}{l} \epsilon_{\mu}\cdot\epsilon_{\nu} = \gamma_{\mu\nu}, \\[1mm] \epsilon^{\mu}\cdot\epsilon^{\nu} = \gamma^{\mu\nu}, \\[1mm] \epsilon^{\mu}\cdot\epsilon_{\nu} = \delta^{\mu}{}_{\nu}, \end{array}\right\} \tag{7.4}$$

$\gamma_{\mu\nu}$ denoting a coefficient of the square of the line element

$$d\sigma^2 = \gamma_{\mu\nu}dx^{\mu}dx^{\nu}.$$

The relation between the two sets of vectors (ϵ^{μ}) and (i_{α}) will be defined as:

$$\left.\begin{array}{l} \epsilon^{\mu} = h^{\mu}{}_{\alpha}\,i_{\alpha} \\[2mm] \epsilon_{\mu} = h_{\mu\alpha}\,i_{\alpha}, \end{array}\right\} \tag{7.5}$$

or

where the coefficients $(h^{\mu}{}_{\alpha}, h_{\mu\alpha})$ are functions of the coordinates and represent components of the vectors (ϵ^{μ}) along the rectilinear axes (i_{α}). $(h^{\mu}{}_{\alpha})$ with $\mu = 1$–5, is a contravariant vector.

From the relations (7.3), (7.4) and (7.5) it follows that:

$$\epsilon_{\mu}\cdot\epsilon_{\nu} = h_{\mu\alpha}\,i_{\alpha}.h_{\nu\beta}\,i_{\beta} = h_{\mu\alpha}\,h_{\nu\beta}\,\delta_{\alpha\beta}$$

or

$$\gamma_{\mu\nu} = h_{\mu\alpha}\,h_{\nu\alpha}. \tag{7.6}$$

Similarly

$$\gamma^{\mu\nu} = h^{\mu}{}_{\alpha}\,h^{\nu}{}_{\alpha}. \tag{7.7}$$

Since

$$h_{\nu\alpha} = \gamma_{\nu\lambda} h^{\lambda}{}_{\alpha},$$

$$\gamma_{\mu\nu} = \gamma_{\nu\lambda} h_{\mu\alpha} h^{\lambda}{}_{\alpha},$$

multiplying by $\gamma^{\nu\sigma}$,

$$\delta^{\sigma}{}_{\mu} = \delta^{\sigma}{}_{\lambda} h_{\mu\alpha} h^{\lambda}{}_{\alpha} = h_{\mu\alpha} h^{\sigma}{}_{\alpha}. \tag{7.8}$$

A vector with components (A^{μ}) in the curvilinear system and (A_{α}) in the rectilinear system is

$$A = X^{\mu} \epsilon_{\mu} = Z_{\alpha} i_{\alpha}.$$

Thus

$$X^{\mu} h_{\mu\alpha} i_{\alpha} = Z_{\alpha} i_{\alpha}$$

and consequently

$$Z_{\alpha} = h_{\mu\alpha} X^{\mu}. \tag{7.9}$$

On multiplying by $h^{\nu}{}_{\alpha}$,

$$h^{\nu}{}_{\alpha} Z_{\alpha} = h^{\nu}{}_{\alpha} h_{\mu\alpha} X^{\mu} = \delta^{\nu}{}_{\mu} X^{\mu} = X^{\nu}.$$

Thus

$$X^{\nu} = h^{\nu}{}_{\alpha} Z_{\alpha}. \tag{7.10}$$

From (7.9) and (7.10)

$$Z_{\alpha} = h_{\mu\alpha} h^{\mu}{}_{\beta} Z_{\beta}$$

so that

$$h_{\mu\alpha} h^{\mu}{}_{\beta} = \delta_{\alpha\beta}. \tag{7.11}$$

The square of A is defined in the two ways $\gamma_{\mu\nu} X^{\mu} X^{\nu}$ or ΣZ_{α}^{2} and these are equal since

$$\gamma_{\mu\nu} X^{\mu} X^{\nu} = h_{\mu\alpha} X^{\mu} h_{\nu\alpha} X^{\nu}$$

$$= Z_{\alpha} Z_{\alpha} = \Sigma Z_{\alpha}^{2}. \tag{7.12}$$

By means of the relations (7.9) and (7.10) the coordinate elements (dx^{μ}) and (dz_{α}) appropriate to the two systems of axes can be related. dz_{α} is used instead of dx_{α} for the rectilinear element to avoid confusion.

The relations are:

and

$$\left. \begin{array}{l} dx^{\mu} = h^{\mu}{}_{\alpha} dz_{\alpha} \\[2mm] dz_{\alpha} = h_{\mu\alpha} dx^{\mu} \end{array} \right\} \tag{7.13}$$

and from (7.12)

$$ds^{2} = \gamma_{\mu\nu} dx^{\mu} dx^{\nu} = \Sigma dx_{\alpha}^{2}. \tag{7.14}$$

It has appeared from Kaluza's theory that the requirements of physics impose conditions upon the values of the coefficients $(\gamma_{\mu\nu})$

and, in particular, upon those containing the suffix 5. In order to conform with these limitations certain restrictions are now placed upon the coefficients $(h^\mu{}_\alpha, h_{\mu\alpha})$.

It is assumed that the fifth axis i_5 is perpendicular to the four-dimensional continuum in the sense that $\epsilon^m . i_5 = 0$ for values of $m = 1, 2, 3, 4$. Thus

$$h^m{}_5 = 0. \tag{7.15}$$

Similarly the axis ϵ_5 will be supposed to have no components along i_α with $\alpha = 1, 2, 3, 4$. Thus

$$\epsilon_5 . i_a = 0$$

or

$$h_{5a} = 0. \tag{7.16}$$

It is to be noted that the first suffix refers to the indices denoted by μ and indicates a component of a contravariant or covariant vector, while the second suffix refers to a component referred to the rectilinear axes and always occupies the lower second place, whatever the type of quantity to which it is attached.

The value of h_{55} is obtained from the relation $\gamma_{55} = h_{5\alpha} h_{5\alpha}$ and on account of the relation (7.16) this becomes $\gamma_{55} = h_{55} h_{55}$. Thus

$$h_{55} = \sqrt{(\gamma_{55})}. \tag{7.17}$$

Since

$$\gamma_{m5} = h_{m\alpha} h_{5\alpha} = h_{m5} h_{55},$$

$$\gamma_{55} \alpha \phi_m = h_{m5} \sqrt{(\gamma_{55})}$$

or

$$h_{m5} = \sqrt{(\gamma_{55})} \alpha \phi_m. \tag{7.18}$$

In the same way the following components with affix 5 may be obtained. Thus:

$$\left. \begin{array}{l} h^m{}_5 = 0, \quad h_{5a} = 0, \quad h_{55} = \sqrt{(\gamma_{55})}, \\ h^5{}_5 = 1/\sqrt{(\gamma_{55})}, \quad h_{m5} = \sqrt{(\gamma_{55})} \alpha \phi_m, \\ h^5{}_a = -\alpha h_{ma} \phi^m = -\alpha h^m{}_a \phi_m, \quad (m, a = 1, 2, 3, 4). \end{array} \right\} \tag{7.19}$$

The results lead to some simplifications in other coefficients. Thus

$$\gamma^{mn} = g^{mn} = h^m{}_\alpha h^n{}_\alpha = h^m{}_a h^n{}_a \quad (a \neq 5). \tag{7.20}$$

Again

$$\left. \begin{array}{l} h^m{}_\alpha h_{n\alpha} = h^m{}_a h_{na} = \delta^m{}_n \\ h_{ma} h_{na} = g_{mn}, \end{array} \right\} \tag{7.21}$$

and

since

$$h_{m\alpha} h_{n\alpha} = \gamma_{mn} = g_{mn} + \gamma_{55} \alpha^2 \phi_m \phi_n$$

and

$$h_{m5} h_{n5} = \gamma_{55} \alpha^2 \phi_m \phi_n.$$

The values of other coefficients for the case when there is no gravitational field can be obtained from the expressions (7.2). Thus

$$g_{11} = h_{1a}h_{1a} \quad (a = 1,2,3,4)$$

and

$$g_{12} = h_{1a}h_{2a}.$$

Since in this case $g_{11}=1$ and $g_{12}=0$, the relations can be satisfied by placing

$$h_{11} = 1, \quad h_{1a} = 0 \quad \text{if } a \neq 1,$$
$$h_{2a} = 0 \quad \text{if } a \neq 2.$$

In general

$$h_{ma} = \delta_{ma} \quad (m = 1,2,3,4), \tag{7.22}$$

but by reference to the relations (7.19) this is not the case for h_{m5}.

In passing to a theory of matrices by analogy with this geometrical theory, the vectors (ϵ^μ) are replaced by the matrices (γ^μ) and the vectors (i_α) by matrices (E_α), the former having components dependent on the coordinates and the latter having constant components. These constant matrices form a group of five mutually anti-commuting matrices obeying the relations:

$$E_\alpha E_\beta + E_\beta E_\alpha = 2\delta_{\alpha\beta} \tag{7.23}$$

and are thus an example of a set described by Eddington as a pentad.

In the equations (5.1) matrices β^m and γ_5 were introduced in order to relate the (γ^μ) which are characteristic of the five-dimensional continuum with those to be regarded as characteristic of the four-dimensional continuum.

In the absence of a gravitational field the latter contain constant elements and are now to be identified with the matrices (E_α). Thus it is possible to write

$$E_a = \beta_a, \quad E_5 = \beta_{..} \tag{7.24}$$

The matrices γ^μ are now expressed in the form

$$\gamma^\mu = h^\mu{}_\alpha E_\alpha \quad [3] \, [4] \tag{7.25}$$

and hence

$$\gamma^\mu \gamma^\nu + \gamma^\nu \gamma^\mu = h^\mu{}_\alpha h^\nu{}_\beta (E_\alpha E_\beta + E_\beta E_\alpha)$$
$$= 2h^\mu{}_\alpha h^\nu{}_\beta \delta_{\alpha\beta}$$
$$= 2h^\mu{}_\alpha h^\nu{}_\alpha = 2\gamma^{\mu\nu}.$$

Similarly

$$\gamma_\mu \gamma_\nu + \gamma_\nu \gamma_\mu = 2h_{\mu\alpha}h_{\nu\alpha} = 2\gamma_{\mu\nu}$$

and

$$\gamma^\mu \gamma_\nu + \gamma_\nu \gamma^\mu = 2h^\mu{}_\alpha h_{\nu\alpha} = 2\delta^\mu{}_\nu. \tag{7.26}$$

Since $h^m{}_5 = 0$,

$$\gamma^m = h^m{}_\alpha E_\alpha = h^m{}_a E_a \quad (a = 1, 2, 3, 4)$$
$$= \beta^m$$

in agreement with (5.1).

It follows also from the value adopted for h_{m5} (7.19) that

$$h_{ma} E_a = \beta_m \tag{7.27}$$

and consequently

$$\gamma_m = h_{ma} E_a + h_{m5} E_5$$
$$= \beta_m + \sqrt{(\gamma_{55})} \, \alpha\phi_m \beta. \tag{7.28}$$

In the course of deriving the quantum equation from the concept of parallel displacement without change of length in Chapter 5 the operator

$$K^\mu{}_\lambda = \frac{\partial \gamma^\mu}{\partial x^\lambda} + \gamma^\rho \varDelta^\mu_{\rho\lambda} \tag{5.15}$$

occurred. From the relation (5.33) which is satisfied by $K^\mu{}_\lambda$ this operator may take the form

$$K^\mu{}_\lambda = \varDelta_\lambda \gamma^\mu - \gamma^\mu \varDelta_\lambda \tag{5.34}.$$

It may be deduced from equation (5.15) that

$$K_{\nu\lambda} = \gamma_{\nu\mu} K^\mu{}_\lambda = \frac{\partial \gamma_\nu}{\partial x^\lambda} - \gamma_\mu \varDelta^\mu_{\nu\lambda} \tag{7.29}$$

and

$$K_{\nu\lambda} = \varDelta_\lambda \gamma_\nu - \gamma_\nu \varDelta_\lambda. \tag{7.30}$$

The values of the operator $\varDelta_\lambda$ for the five values of λ in the case of constant matrices, i.e. in the absence of a gravitational field, have been given in the relations (5.36) and (5.37).

But it is now possible to derive their values in the more general case of variable matrices in terms of the coefficients $(h^\mu{}_\alpha)$ and $(h_{\mu\alpha})$. The value of $K^\mu{}_\lambda$ or $K_{\mu\lambda}$ can then be derived and the significance of the law $K^\mu{}_\mu = 0$ (5.16) becomes apparent, for it takes its place in the geometrical description of the world of microscopic phenomena as Einstein's law of gravitation does in the macroscopic world.

In the first place the coefficient $\varDelta^\mu_{\nu\lambda}$ is expressed in terms of the coefficients $(h^\mu{}_\alpha)$ and $(h_{\mu\alpha})$.

$$\varDelta^\mu_{\nu\lambda} = \tfrac{1}{2}\gamma^{\mu\rho}\left(\frac{\partial \gamma_{\nu\rho}}{\partial x^\lambda} + \frac{\partial \gamma_{\lambda\rho}}{\partial x^\nu} - \frac{\partial \gamma_{\nu\lambda}}{\partial x^\rho}\right).$$

On substitution by means of $\gamma_{\nu\rho}=h_{\nu\alpha}h_{\rho\alpha}$, etc., and $\gamma^{\mu\rho}=h^\mu{}_\alpha h^\rho{}_\alpha$, the result

$$2\Delta^\mu_{\nu\lambda} = h^\mu{}_\alpha\left(\frac{\partial h_{\nu\alpha}}{\partial x^\lambda}+\frac{\partial h_{\lambda\alpha}}{\partial x^\nu}\right)+\gamma^{\mu\rho}\gamma_{\nu\sigma}h^\sigma{}_\alpha\left(\frac{\partial h_{\rho\alpha}}{\partial x^\lambda}-\frac{\partial h_{\lambda\alpha}}{\partial x^\rho}\right)$$

$$+\gamma^{\mu\rho}\gamma_{\lambda\sigma}h^\sigma{}_\alpha\left(\frac{\partial h_{\rho\alpha}}{\partial x^\nu}-\frac{\partial h_{\nu\alpha}}{\partial x^\rho}\right)$$

is obtained.

Write

$$P^\mu_{\nu\lambda} = h^\mu{}_\alpha\frac{\partial h_{\nu\alpha}}{\partial x^\lambda}, \quad \Lambda^\mu_{\nu\lambda} = P^\mu_{\nu\lambda}-P^\mu_{\lambda\nu} = h^\mu{}_\alpha\left(\frac{\partial h_{\nu\alpha}}{\partial x^\lambda}-\frac{\partial h_{\lambda\alpha}}{\partial x^\nu}\right)$$

then

$$2\Delta^\mu_{\nu\lambda} = P^\mu_{\nu\lambda}+P^\mu_{\lambda\nu}+\gamma^{\mu\rho}\gamma_{\nu\sigma}\Lambda^\sigma_{\rho\lambda}+\gamma^{\mu\rho}\gamma_{\lambda\sigma}\Lambda^\sigma_{\rho\nu}.$$

Since

$$h^\mu{}_\alpha h_{\nu\alpha} = \delta^\mu{}_\nu, \quad P^\mu_{\nu\lambda} = -h_{\mu\alpha}\frac{\partial h^\mu{}_\alpha}{\partial x^\lambda}.$$

By means of these relations it can be shown that

$$K_{\nu\lambda} = \frac{\partial\gamma_\nu}{\partial x^\lambda}-\Delta^\mu_{\nu\lambda}\gamma_\mu = \tfrac{1}{2}(\gamma_{\lambda\sigma}\Lambda^\sigma_{\nu\mu}+\gamma_{\nu\sigma}\Lambda^\sigma_{\lambda\mu}+\gamma_{\mu\sigma}\Lambda^\sigma_{\nu\lambda})\gamma^\mu. \quad (7.31)$$

The form of $K_{\nu\lambda}$,

$$K_{\nu\lambda} = \Delta_\lambda\gamma_\nu-\gamma_\nu\Delta_\lambda$$

and the relation (4.19),

$$s^{\mu\nu}\gamma^\lambda-\gamma^\lambda s^{\mu\nu} = 2(\gamma^{\lambda\nu}\gamma^\mu-\gamma^{\lambda\mu}\gamma^\nu)$$

or

$$s^{\mu\rho}\gamma_\nu-\gamma_\nu s^{\mu\rho} = 2(\gamma^\mu\delta^\rho{}_\nu-\gamma^\rho\delta^\mu{}_\nu),$$

suggest that a solution for Δ_λ should be sought in the form:

$$\Delta_\lambda = F_{\lambda\mu\rho}s^{\mu\rho}, \quad (7.32)$$

$F_{\lambda\mu\rho}$, like $s^{\mu\rho}$, being antisymmetric symmetric in μ and ρ. With this form for Δ_λ,

$$\Delta_\lambda\gamma_\nu-\gamma_\nu\Delta_\lambda = F_{\lambda\mu\rho}(s^{\mu\rho}\gamma_\nu-\gamma_\nu s^{\mu\rho}) = 2F_{\lambda\mu\rho}(\gamma^\mu\delta^\rho{}_\nu-\gamma^\rho\delta^\mu{}_\nu)$$

$$= 2(F_{\lambda\mu\nu}\gamma^\mu-F_{\lambda\nu\rho}\gamma^\rho) = 2(F_{\lambda\mu\nu}-F_{\lambda\nu\mu})\gamma^\mu$$

$$= 4F_{\lambda\mu\nu}\gamma^\mu.$$

Thus the relation (7.31) is satisfied if

$$F_{\lambda\mu\nu} = \tfrac{1}{8}(\gamma_{\lambda\sigma}\Lambda^\sigma_{\nu\mu}+\gamma_{\nu\sigma}\Lambda^\sigma_{\lambda\mu}+\gamma_{\mu\sigma}\Lambda^\sigma_{\nu\lambda}), \quad (7.33)$$

and since $\Lambda^{\sigma}_{\nu\mu} = -\Lambda^{\sigma}_{\mu\nu}$, the expression for Δ_{λ} may be written as

$$\Delta_{\lambda} = \tfrac{1}{8}(-\gamma_{\lambda\sigma}\Lambda^{\sigma}_{\mu\nu}+\gamma_{\mu\sigma}\Lambda^{\sigma}_{\nu\lambda}+\gamma_{\nu\sigma}\Lambda^{\sigma}_{\lambda\mu})\,s^{\mu\nu}. \quad [5] \qquad (7.34)$$

The relation (7.31) is also satisfied if a quantity H_{λ}, which commutes with the matrices γ_{λ}, be added to Δ_{λ}, for example, if H_{λ} is an ordinary quantity.

The values of the operator Δ_{λ} for the five values of λ can be obtained for the case when the gravitational field is neglected by the substitution of the values of $(h^{\mu}{}_{\alpha}, h_{\mu\alpha})$ given in the equations (7.19) and (7.22). The results obtained will be found to agree with those of equations (5.36) and (5.37).

The expression for $K_{\nu\lambda}$ (7.30) now becomes

$$K_{\nu\lambda} = F_{\lambda\mu\rho}(s^{\mu\rho}\gamma_{\nu}-\gamma_{\nu}s^{\mu\rho}), \qquad (7.35)$$

$F_{\lambda\mu\rho}$ being given by (7.33).

The assumption $K^{\mu}{}_{\mu}=0$, stated as a law of the microscopic world, can now be expressed as a limitation placed upon the coefficients $(h^{\mu}{}_{\alpha})$, which may be regarded as a restriction upon the basis of the system of location.

From equation (7.36) it follows that

$$\begin{aligned}
K^{\nu}{}_{\nu} &= F_{\nu\mu\rho}(s^{\mu\rho}\gamma^{\nu}-\gamma^{\nu}s^{\mu\rho}) \\
&= 2F_{\nu\mu\rho}(\gamma^{\nu\rho}\gamma^{\mu}-\gamma^{\nu\mu}\gamma^{\rho}) \\
&= 2(F_{\nu\mu\rho}\gamma^{\nu\rho}\gamma^{\mu}-F_{\nu\rho\mu}\gamma^{\nu\rho}\gamma^{\mu}),
\end{aligned}$$

interchanging μ and ρ in the second term.

Since $F_{\nu\mu\rho}=-F_{\nu\rho\mu}$, this becomes

$$\begin{aligned}
K^{\nu}{}_{\nu} &= 4\gamma^{\nu\rho}F_{\nu\mu\rho}\gamma^{\mu} \\
&= \tfrac{1}{2}(\gamma^{\nu\rho}\gamma_{\nu\sigma}\Lambda^{\sigma}_{\rho\mu}+\gamma^{\nu\rho}\gamma_{\rho\sigma}\Lambda^{\sigma}_{\nu\mu}+\gamma^{\nu\rho}\gamma_{\mu\sigma}\Lambda^{\sigma}_{\rho\nu}).
\end{aligned}$$

The third term in the bracket vanishes because $\gamma^{\nu\rho}$ is symmetrical in ν and ρ and $\Lambda^{\sigma}_{\rho\nu}$ is antisymmetrical in these indices. The first and second terms are equal to

$$\delta^{\rho}{}_{\sigma}\Lambda^{\sigma}_{\rho\mu}+\delta^{\nu}{}_{\sigma}\Lambda^{\sigma}_{\nu\mu} = 2\Lambda^{\rho}_{\rho\mu}.$$

Thus

$$\left.\begin{aligned}
K^{\nu}{}_{\nu} &= \Lambda^{\rho}_{\rho\mu}\gamma^{\mu} \\
&= h^{\rho}{}_{\alpha}\left(\frac{\partial h_{\rho\alpha}}{\partial x^{\mu}}-\frac{\partial h_{\mu\alpha}}{\partial x^{\rho}}\right)\gamma^{\mu}.
\end{aligned}\right\} \qquad (7.36)$$

Thus the condition $K^{\nu}{}_{\nu}=0$ becomes

$$h^{\rho}{}_{\alpha}\left(\frac{\partial h_{\rho\alpha}}{\partial x^{\mu}}-\frac{\partial h_{\mu\alpha}}{\partial x^{\rho}}\right)\gamma^{\mu}=0. \qquad (7.37)$$

This shows the significance of the law $K^{\nu}{}_{\nu}=0$ and since this operator vanishes identically with constant values of the coefficients $(h^{\rho}{}_{\alpha}, h_{\rho\alpha})$, the fact that the law is of a geometrical character, placing a condition on the components $(h^{\mu}{}_{\alpha})$, does not appear until an attempt is made to express the law in the notation of the general theory of relativity.

Bibliography

1. A. EINSTEIN, 1931. *Sber. preuss. Akad. Wiss.*, **25**, 541.
2. H. T. FLINT, 1928. *Proc. R. Soc.* A, **121**, 676.
   H. T. FLINT, 1933. *Proc. R. Soc.* A, **141**, 364.
3. V. BARGMANN, 1932. *Sber. preuss. Akad. Wiss.*, XXIV.
4. H. W. HASKEY, 1940. *Phil. Mag.* Ser. 7, XXX, 478.
5. H. W. HASKEY, 1945. *Proc. Edinb. math. Soc.*, Ser. 2, **7**, IV 174.

Index